3-MINUTE EINSTEIN

3-MINUTE EINSTEIN

Digesting his life, theories, and influence in 3-minute morsels

Paul Parsons

Foreword by **John Gribbin**

METRO BOOKS
NEW YORK

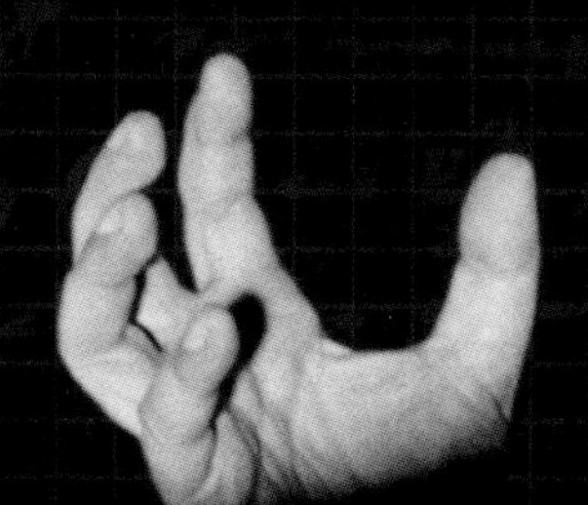

This 2011 edition published by
Metro Books by arrangement with
Ivy Press

This book was conceived, designed, and produced by
Ivy Press
210 High Street, Lewes,
East Sussex BN7 2NS, U.K.
www.ivy-group.co.uk

CREATIVE DIRECTOR Peter Bridgewater
PUBLISHER Jason Hook
EDITORIAL DIRECTOR Caroline Earle
ART DIRECTOR Michael Whitehead
DESIGNER Glyn Bridgewater
ASSISTANT EDITOR Jamie Pumfrey

Metro Books
122 Fifth Avenue
New York, NY 10011

ISBN-13: 978-1-4351-3002-9

Printed and bound in China
Color Origination by Ivy Press Reprographics

Cover image: Bettmann/Corbis.

10 9 8 7 6 5 4 3 2 1

Contents

Foreword

Everyone has heard of Albert Einstein, but few people have a clear idea of what his theories are all about. Paul Parsons is one of the people who does understand Einstein's theories, and in this ingenious book he has found a way to make them accessible even to people who struggled with mathematics at school. By breaking the story up into bite-sized pieces that can be absorbed individually, instead of forcing the reader to plow through pages of text to get to the nuggets of truth, he has made it easy to absorb the facts while still taking care not to distort the science.

The two relativity theories naturally take pride of place (and it may be a surprise to some readers to find out that there are indeed two such theories, not one), making it clear how time is distorted by travel and how space is distorted by gravity. But the less well-known aspects of Einstein's science are not neglected, so we also find out how the great man's contributions helped in the invention of lasers, how he patented a unique kind of refrigerator, how he proved atoms exist, and how he spent his last years in a premature search for a "theory of everything"—fifty years ahead of his time.

One of the most amazing things about Einstein's achievements though, is that they were carried out in spite of a private life often in turmoil. While still a student, he fathered an illegitimate child. His first marriage ended in divorce; and even during his second marriage, he had many affairs. What is widely regarded as his greatest work, the general theory of relativity (which is, among other things, the theory of black holes and the Universe) was completed in Berlin during the First World War, where there was little food and for a time Einstein was dangerously ill. And just when he ought to have been able to settle down to a quiet life as the Grand Old Man of German science, the rise of the Nazis forced him to flee to the United States where, ironically, for a time he was under suspicion of being a communist.

All of this provides ample material for several full-length books, most of which I have read. But nobody, as far as I am aware, has told the story of Einstein so succinctly while also being so accurate (or, indeed, so accurately while also being so succinct!) as Parsons does. And one of the great joys of this approach is that you can open the book anywhere and pick out some nugget of information about Einstein's life or his work, since virtually each page is completely self-contained and stands alone. Even if you think you already know about Einstein and his work, you will find something to intrigue you here; and if you are not familiar with his life and times, there is no better place to start.

JOHN GRIBBIN
Visiting Fellow in Astronomy
University of Sussex, UK

How the Book Works

This book tells the story of Albert Einstein in three parts. The first chapter details Einstein's life, from his birth in the late nineteenth century in the south of Germany, through his life as a young Jewish boy, his later move to study in Switzerland, the return to Germany as a physics professor, and his ultimate emigration to the United States following Hitler's rise to power. The second chapter looks at Einstein's theories. His two theories of relativity turned out to be cornerstones of twentieth-century physics. But there's also a wealth of information about his lesser-known contributions to science—predicting the particle nature of light, investigating the fundamental properties of matter, and explaining the photoelectric effect, which was the foundation for solar energy. The final chapter takes stock of Einstein's influence—the legacy he left, not just in relation to science but for technology, philosophy, politics, and the shape of the world at large.

3-minute Einstein

Each chapter of the book is made up of twenty 3-minute features. So, for example, in the Theories chapter you'll find separate features on the special theory of relativity, black holes, the quantum world, and many more. Every feature has three paragraphs, each dealing with one aspect of that topic. For instance, the feature on black holes has paragraphs on "dark stars" (the musings about what eventually became known as black holes), "horizons and singularities" (looking at the structure of black holes and how they work), and "wormholes" (a bizarre kind of black hole that it might actually be possible to travel through). A single paragraph will take you about one minute to digest, and so each feature can be read in about three minutes. So, 3-minute Einstein*!*

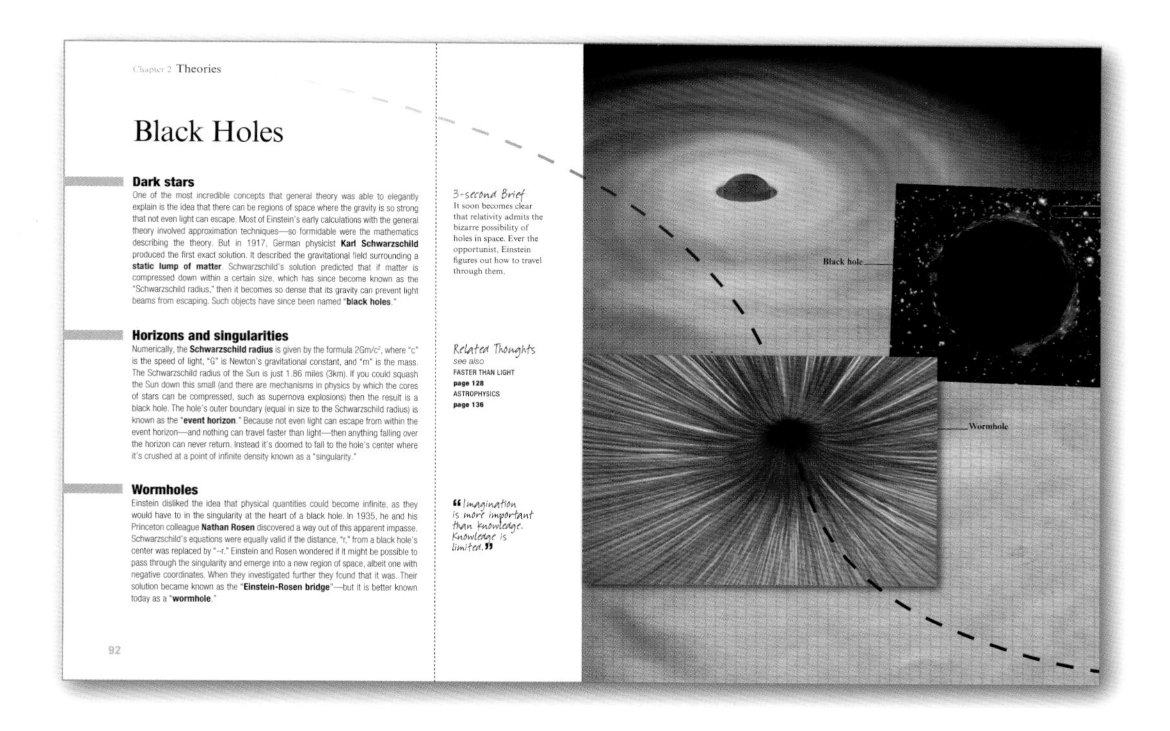

Chapter 2 Theories

Black Holes

Dark stars

One of the most incredible concepts that general theory was able to elegantly explain is the idea that there can be regions of space where the gravity is so strong that not even light can escape. Most of Einstein's early calculations with the general theory involved approximation techniques—so formidable were the mathematics describing the theory. But in 1917, German physicist **Karl Schwarzschild** produced the first exact solution. It described the gravitational field surrounding a **static lump of matter**. Schwarzschild's solution predicted that if matter is compressed down within a certain size, which has since become known as the "Schwarzschild radius," then it becomes so dense that its gravity can prevent light beams from escaping. Such objects have since been named "**black holes**."

Horizons and singularities

Numerically, the **Schwarzschild radius** is given by the formula $2Gm/c^2$, where "c" is the speed of light, "G" is Newton's gravitational constant, and "m" is the mass. The Schwarzschild radius of the Sun is just 1.86 miles (3km). If you could squash the Sun down this small (and there are mechanisms in physics by which the cores of stars can be compressed, such as supernova explosions) then the result is a black hole. The hole's outer boundary (equal in size to the Schwarzschild radius) is known as the "**event horizon**." Because not even light can escape from within the event horizon—and nothing can travel faster than light—then anything falling over the horizon can never return. Instead it's doomed to fall to the hole's center where it's crushed at a point of infinite density known as a "singularity."

Wormholes

Einstein disliked the idea that physical quantities could become infinite, as they would have to in the singularity at the heart of a black hole. In 1935, he and his Princeton colleague **Nathan Rosen** discovered a way out of this apparent impasse. Schwarzschild's equations were equally valid if the distance, "r," from a black hole's center was replaced by "–r." Einstein and Rosen wondered if it might be possible to pass through the singularity and emerge into a new region of space, albeit one with negative coordinates. When they investigated further they found that it was. Their solution became known as the "**Einstein-Rosen bridge**"—but it is better known today as a "**wormhole**."

92

3-second Brief

It soon becomes clear that relativity admits the bizarre possibility of holes in space. Ever the opportunist, Einstein figures out how to travel through them.

Related Thoughts

see also

FASTER THAN LIGHT

page 128

ASTROPHYSICS

page 136

"Imagination is more important than knowledge. Knowledge is limited."

Instant expert

This structure means that each of the three chapters will take about an hour to digest, and that the whole book will furnish you with the life history and career highlights of Albert Einstein in about three hours. In addition to all that, each chapter concludes with a timeline and glossary to help you keep your thoughts in order. It won't make you a genius like Einstein, but in a single evening's reading you will discover the life story, scientific achievements, and lasting legacy of one of the greatest geniuses ever to tread the planet.

Introduction

Albert Einstein was the definitive genius of our age. His droopy features, sparkling eyes, and crazy hair have become the hallmarks of the man who gave us theories of relativity and $E=mc^2$, while his name alone has become a metaphor for intellectual brilliance. But Einstein was so much more. Not only did his general and special theory of relativity lay bare the esoteric mysteries of space and time, his breakthroughs gave us everything from solar power, to computers and fiber-optic communications, and even Blu-ray players. Virtually everyone in the developed world has something to thank him for. And his genius wasn't merely confined to science. He was active politically—campaigning for the establishment of a homeland for the Jews—and became a prominent figure in the peace movement following the atomic bombings at the end of the Second World War, for which he felt partially responsible. For many though, it was Einstein's qualities as a human being that endeared him the most. He became a fierce critic of authoritarianism, prejudice, and conformity, and a champion of free speech, free thinking, and individualism. Most of all, throughout his life Einstein retained a deep-seated sense of humility, often stating when asked about his great achievements: "I have no special talents; I am only passionately curious."

Iconic archetype

Einstein's untidy hair and distinctive features were a gift to cartoonists, and his fame was such that he would pretend to be someone else so as to avoid having to explain his theories to passersby who recognized him in the street.

Budding genius

Einstein was born in the German city of Ulm on March 14, 1879, the son of an electrical engineer. He showed an early talent for mathematics and wrote his first scientific paper in 1895.

Young scientist

From 1903 Einstein worked in the patent office in Bern, and he didn't hold an academic post until 1908. He did publish scientific papers while at the patent office, including four in 1905 that were fundamental to the development of modern physics.

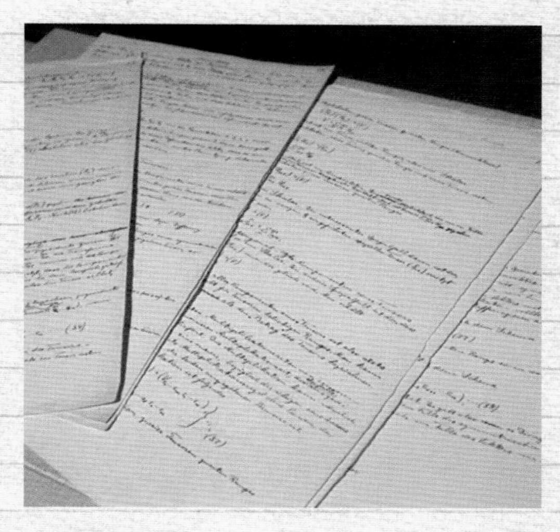

Scientific notebooks

Many of Einstein's old scientific notebooks have been kept as part of his literary estate. They offer a fascinating glimpse of Einstein's mind at work as he tried to slot the final pieces into his general theory of relativity.

Marriage and divorce

Einstein was married twice. His first wife was Mileva Maric, whom he married in 1903, and they had two sons, Hans Albert and Eduard. Einstein and Mileva were divorced in 1919—the same year that Einstein married his second wife, Elsa (pictured).

Celebrity status

Einstein with Charlie Chaplin attending the Hollywood premiere of Chaplin's movie City Lights *in 1931. The success of his theories of relativity made Einstein one of the few scientists to become a household name.*

Feted

In 1929, Albert Einstein received the Max Planck Medal of the German Physical Society—presented by Planck himself. He also received the Nobel Prize in Physics in 1921 and the Royal Society's prestigious Copley Medal in 1925.

Musical inspiration

Einstein was passionate about music and became a talented violinist at an early age. Later in life, he would often lose himself in music as a source of inspiration when working on difficult problems in physics.

Ladies' man

Gravity wasn't the only force of attraction in Einstein's life—in addition to his two marriages he is believed to have had many affairs. This photograph, taken in 1932, shows Einstein amid a crowd of admirers.

Refugee in England

When Hitler came to power in Germany in 1933, the Jewish Einstein was forced to flee the country. He stayed in England briefly, at the invitation of Commander Oliver Locker-Lampson who assigned three armed bodyguards to look after him.

US citizen

Einstein was handed his certificate of American citizenship by Judge Phillip Forman on October 1, 1940—having been in residence in Princeton, New Jersey, since October 1933.

Brilliant speaker

Einstein addresses the Eighth American Scientific Congress at Princeton in May 1940. Although a brilliant physicist, his shambolic approach meant that he was not known for his skill as a lecturer—and yet there was rarely an empty seat in the house.

Free spirit

Albert Einstein sailing at Saranac Lake, New York, during August 1945. Sailing was one of Einstein's great passions—although on at least one occasion he had to be rescued by the Coast Guard.

Peace campaigner

Following the atomic bombing of Hiroshima and Nagasaki in 1945, Einstein helped to found the Emergency Committee of Atomic Scientists (pictured here), which campaigned for nuclear arms control.

Activist

Einstein was a supporter of the Zionist movement, campaigning for a homeland for the Jewish people. After the State of Israel was established, its first Prime Minister, David Ben-Gurion, visited Einstein in 1951.

Eccentric

It's not something that many scientists would be seen doing today, let alone in 1951. But Einstein's impromptu reaction to a press photographer was characteristically unconventional—and has become an iconic image.

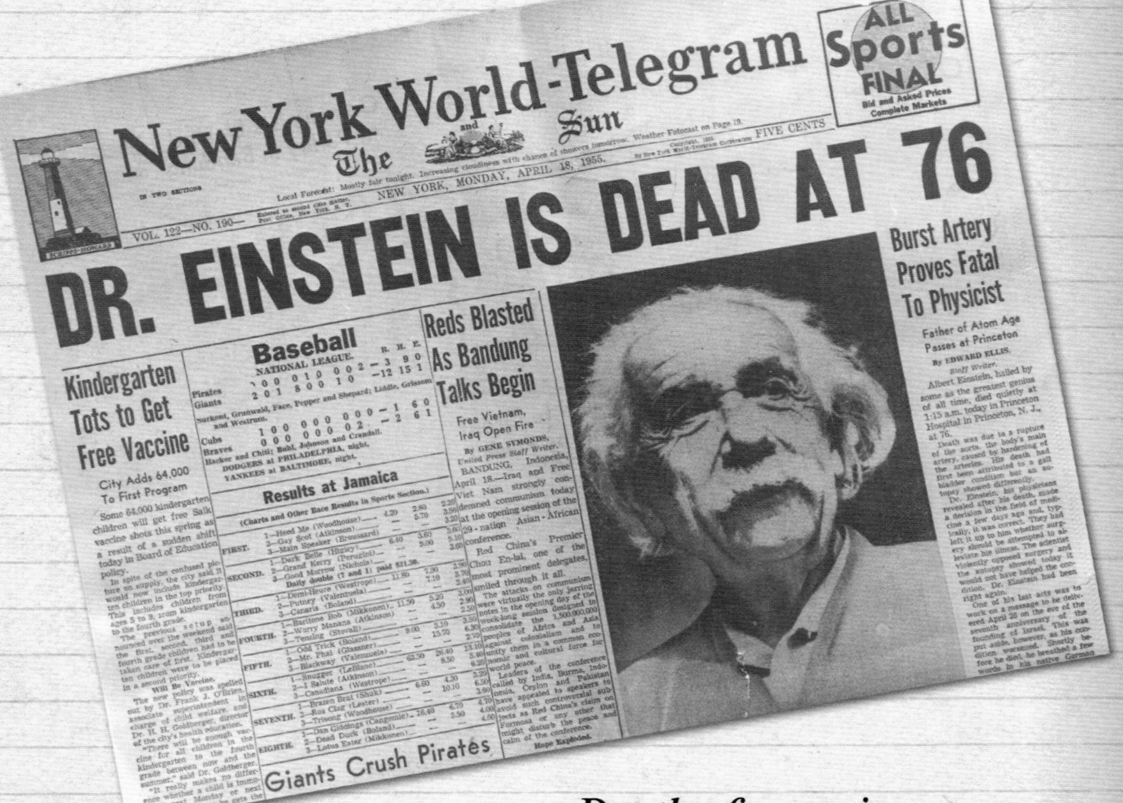

New York World-Telegram
The Sun
ALL Sports FINAL
Bid and Asked Prices
Complete Markets

VOL. 122—NO. 190— NEW YORK, MONDAY, APRIL 18, 1955. FIVE CENTS

DR. EINSTEIN IS DEAD AT 76

Kindergarten Tots to Get Free Vaccine

City Adds 64,000 To First Program

Some 64,000 kindergarten children will get free Salk vaccine shots this spring as a result of a sudden shift today in Board of Education policy.

In spite of the confused picture on supply, the city said it would now include kindergarten children in the top priority. This includes children from ages 5 to 9, from kindergarten to the fourth grade.

The previous setup announced over the weekend said the first, second, third and fourth grade children had to be taken care of first. Kindergarten children were to be placed in a second priority.

Will Be Vaccine.

The new policy was spelled out by Dr. Frank J. O'Brien, associate superintendent in charge of child welfare, and Dr. H. H. Goldberger, director of the city's health education.

"There will be enough vaccine for all children in the kindergarten to the fourth grade between now and the summer," said Dr. Goldberger.

"It really makes no difference whether a child is immunized next Monday or next month, as long as he gets the

Baseball

NATIONAL LEAGUE.

		R.	H.	E.
Pirates	100 010 002	3	9	0
Giants	201 800 10	12	15	1

Surkont, Grunwald, Face, Pepper and Shepard; Liddle, Grissom and Westrum.

		R.	H.	E.
Cubs	100 000 000	1	6	0
Braves	000 000 02	2	6	1

Hacker and Chiti; Buhl, Johnson and Crandall.

DODGERS at PHILADELPHIA, night.
YANKEES at BALTIMORE, night.

Results at Jamaica

(Charts and Other Race Results in Sports Section.)

Race	Horse (Jockey)			
FIRST.	1—Heed Me (Woodhouse)	4.20	2.80	2.20
	2—Gay Scot (Atkinson)	—	5.70	3.50
	3—Main Speaker (Broussard)	—	—	3.20
SECOND.	1—Dark Belle (Higley)	6.40	3.80	3.00
	2—Grand Kerry (Perugini)	—	9.00	5.10
	3—Good Morrow (Nichols)	—	—	3.60
	Daily double (7 and 1) paid $21.30.			
THIRD.	1—Demi-Heure (Westrope)	11.80	7.30	3.90
	2—Putney (Valenzuela)	—	7.10	3.70
	3—Canaris (Boland)	—	—	2.40
FOURTH.	1—Baritone Bob (Mikkonen)	11.30	8.20	3.00
	2—Worry Manana (Atkinson)	—	4.50	2.90
	3—Tenzing (Stovall)	—	—	2.30
FIFTH.	1—Odd Trick (Boland)	9.00	5.10	3.50
	2—Mr. Phat (Glassner)	—	15.70	6.30
	3—Blackway (Valenzuela)	—	—	2.70
SIXTH.	1—Snuggee (LeBlanc)	63.50	26.40	13.10
	2—I Salute (Atkinson)	—	8.50	5.40
	3—Canadiana (Westrope)	—	—	6.20
SEVENTH.	1—Brazen Brat (Shuk)	6.60	4.30	3.20
	2—Ros Clag (Lester)	—	10.10	6.50
	3—Trisong (Woodhouse)	—	—	3.60
EIGHTH.	1—Dan Giddings (Cangemie)	16.40	6.70	4.70
	2—Dead Duck (Boland)	—	5.50	4.00
	3—Lotus Eater (Mikkonen)	—	—	4.00

Giants Crush Pirates

Reds Blasted As Bandung Talks Begin

Free Vietnam, Iraq Open Fire

By GENE SYMONDS,
United Press Staff Writer.

BANDUNG, Indonesia, April 18.—Iraq and Free Viet Nam strongly condemned communism today at the opening session of the 29-nation Asian-African conference.

Red China's Premier Chou En-lai, one of the most prominent delegates, smiled through it all.

The attacks on communism were virtually the only jarring notes in the opening day of the week-long session designed to consolidate the 1,500,000,000 peoples of Africa and Asia against colonialism and to unify them in a common economic and cultural force for world peace.

Leaders of the conference called by India, Burma, Indonesia, Ceylon and Pakistan have appealed to speakers to avoid such controversial subjects as Red China's claim on Formosa or any other that might disturb the peace and calm of the conference.

Hope Exploded.

Burst Artery Proves Fatal To Physicist

Father of Atom Age Passes at Princeton

By EDWARD ELLIS,
Staff Writer.

Albert Einstein, hailed by some as the greatest genius of all time, died quietly at 1:15 a.m. today in Princeton Hospital in Princeton, N. J., at 76.

Death was due to a rupture of the aorta, the body's main artery, caused by hardening of the arteries. His death had first been attributed to a gall bladder condition but an autopsy showed differently.

Dr. Einstein, his physicians revealed after his death, made a decision in the field of medicine a few days ago and, typically, it was correct. They had left it up to him whether surgery should be attempted to alleviate his illness. The scientist violently opposed surgery and the autopsy showed today it would not have helped the condition. Dr. Einstein had been right again.

One of his last acts was to work on a message to be delivered April 20 on the eve of the seventh anniversary of the founding of Israel. This was put aside, however, as his condition worsened. Shortly before he died, he breathed a few words in his native German

Death of a genius

Einstein died of a burst aortic aneurysm on April 18, 1955. Right up until the end, he carried on working from his hospital bed. His body was cremated later on the same day.

Legacy

Einstein's vacated office at the Institute of Advanced Study in Princeton, New Jersey, on the day of his death. His legacy—to science, technology, world peace, and even politics—was immeasurable.

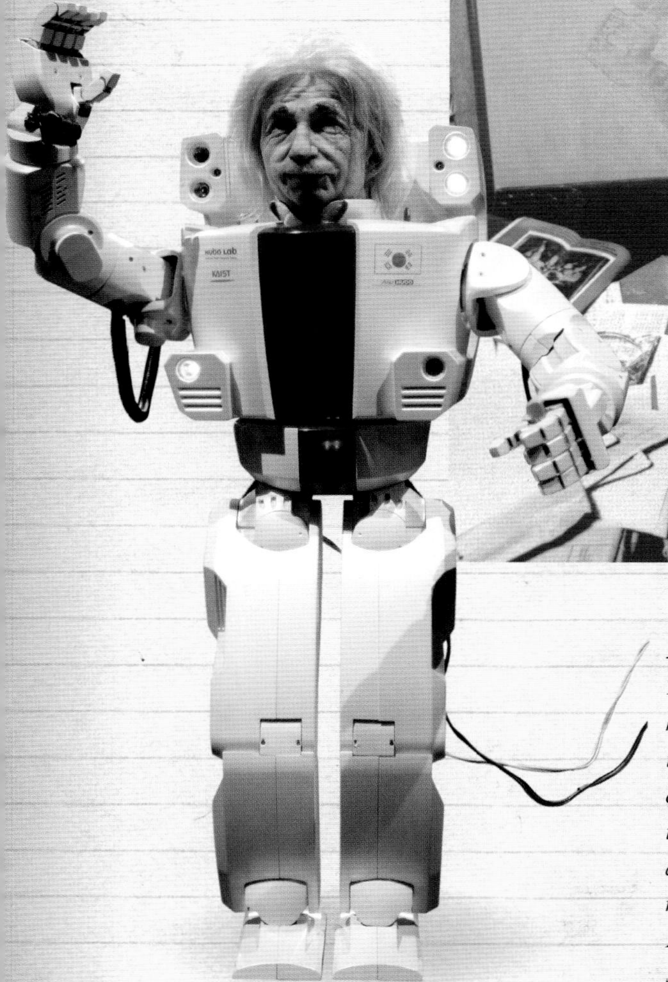

Lasting influence

More than five decades after his death, Einstein remains the blueprint for the lovable eccentric genius. His likeness is used here on "Albert Hubo," a humanoid robot built by researchers at the Korea Advanced Institute of Science and Technology.

MONACO

1,70

1879-1979

ALBERT EINSTEIN

Chapter 1

Life

The Beginning

Birth

Albert Einstein's parents can have had no idea of the extent to which the world would be changed by the tiny bundle they brought into existence at 11:30 a.m. on **March 14, 1879**. The boy was born in **Ulm**, an ancient city in the southwestern corner of Germany's new Reich. Initially his parents wanted to name him Abraham—after his grandfather—but they decided this sounded too Jewish (although Jewish by descent, they themselves had little interest in religion) and so they changed it to **Albert**. It was a name that would become forever etched into the annals of history.

The folks

Einstein's father, **Hermann**, was born in the German town of Buchau in 1847. When Albert was born, Hermann was a partner in a feather-bed store in Ulm. His mother was **Pauline Koch**, born in 1858 in Cannstatt, a German town just outside Stuttgart. The two were married in 1876, when Pauline was just 18. In 1880, Hermann abandoned his ailing feather-bed business and went into partnership with his brother, Jakob, to set up a company manufacturing electrical equipment, such as generators and electric lighting, called Einstein & Cie. The family moved to **Munich** where the business was operated. Sadly, though, it never brought in the riches that Hermann had hoped for. He died in 1902. Pauline lived until 1920.

Einstein's sister

Hermann and Pauline Einstein only had one other child—Maria, or "**Maja**" as she was affectionately known, who was born two years after Albert, in 1881. When Albert was first introduced to her, he is reported to have said, "Where are the wheels?" believing her to be some sort of new toy for him. The two would become dear friends as well as siblings. Following the rise of fascism in Europe during the 1930s, Maja followed Albert and many other Jews to the **United States**, settling close to her brother in Princeton in 1939. Her health began to decline in 1946, following a stroke. She died in 1951 from atherosclerosis—blocked arteries. Einstein wrote in a letter: "I miss her more than can be imagined."

3-second Brief

Einstein was born in 1879. It was the same year that Edison first demonstrated electric light and the British battled the African Zulus at Rorke's Drift.

Related Thoughts

see also
SWITZERLAND
page 26
EINSTEIN'S CHILDREN
page 34
COMING TO AMERICA
page 50

"We never cease to stand like curious children before the great Mystery into which we were born."

Munich City Hall

Maximilianeum, Munich

Young Einstein, 1882

Childhood

Slow talker

For the child destined to grow into probably the **greatest scientist** who ever lived, Albert Einstein made a rather faltering start in life. He was a very late talker, not uttering his first words until past the age of two. Some thought he was retarded and the Einsteins' housemaid even called him "the dopey one." Even when he did finally speak, he developed an odd habit of repeating under his breath every sentence that he spoke. This tendency stayed with him to some degree for the rest of his life. Some have suggested that Einstein's early difficulty with words may explain his preference for **thinking in pictures**, which was instrumental in some of his greatest scientific breakthroughs.

School days

The young Einstein attended a Catholic school near the family home. He was a loner as a child, preferring to spend his time creating objects with his construction set or simply daydreaming, rather than joining in with group games. At the age of nine he went to high school, attending the **Luitpold Gymnasium** in the center of Munich. Here the studious young Einstein took naturally to science and math, getting to grips with calculus, a technique for studying how quantities change with time, by age 15. It was at school that Einstein's famous **disregard for authority** first demonstrated itself, making him unpopular with many of his teachers.

The young musician

The young Albert displayed musical talent from an early age. His mother, herself an excellent pianist, sent him for **violin lessons** and Einstein soon became a keen and accomplished violinist, developing a deep love of classical music, his favorite composer being **Mozart**. Music remained a passion for Einstein throughout his life. During his 20s he once reportedly burst in on a neighbor whom he had heard playing Mozart on the piano, simply so he could accompany on violin. He is also believed to have played a duet with astronomer and television presenter Sir Patrick Moore—but, alas, there is no known recording of it. Music wasn't merely a pastime for Einstein; it served as an **inspiration**, aiding his concentration and creativity.

3-second Brief

After conquering an early difficulty with speech, the young Einstein excels at math, science, and music. From an early age, he is a loner and a rebel.

Related Thoughts

see also
ZURICH POLYTECHNIC
page 28
EINSTEIN'S PHILOSOPHY
page 102

"Intellectual growth should commence at birth and cease only at death."

Mozart
Mechanical geometry
y
D
T
3''
C
P
U
N
3'
2''
2'
1'
1''
O
A
1°
2°
1

The Fledgling Genius

Einstein's compass

When Einstein was very young—around the age of four or five—his father gave him a **navigational compass** as a gift. He became fixated by the way the needle would move in response to a seemingly invisible force—the magnetic field of the Earth. This "action at a distance" effect of fields—most notably that of the **gravitational field**, a force exerted by the masses of heavy objects such as **stars** and planets—would become a central strand in his later scientific investigations. It would lead Einstein directly to his **general theory of relativity**, arguably his greatest achievement and still the best working theory of gravity. It also prompted him to spend much of his later life in pursuit of a unified field theory that would bring together all the known fields of nature under one banner.

Constant reader

Albert's early interest in science was fueled further in the late 1880s by a young man named **Max Talmud**. This struggling medical student would come once a week to the Einsteins' home to share a meal with the family (a Jewish custom). Noticing Albert's budding intellect and fascination with the **workings of nature**, Talmud would bring **science books** for the boy to read. The wide-eyed 10-year-old worked his way voraciously through the great popular science works of the day. When he had devoured all of Talmud's science books he moved on to math, geometry, and then philosophy. Years later, in 1921, Einstein met Talmud again—now going by the westernized surname "Talmey"—during a visit to New York.

Cycling with light

In 1895, the 16-year-old Einstein was seized by one of the most important thoughts in his entire life. He wondered what it might be like to ride a **bicycle** alongside a **light beam**. If light moved like everyday objects, then, relative to Einstein on his bike, the beam should appear to be at rest, frozen in space. As Einstein would discover, the truth was quite the opposite. Ten years later, this simple germ of an idea led him to develop a theory that would cause a revolution in the way we think about light, fast-moving objects, and the very nature of **space and time**.

3-second Brief

Adolescent Einstein is inspired by the way a compass needle moves, while a bike ride at the age of just 16 sets him on the road to relativity.

Related Thoughts

see also

FOUNDATIONS OF THE SPECIAL THEORY
page 74

FOUNDATIONS OF THE GENERAL THEORY
page 80

UNIFIED FIELD THEORY
page 100

"As a boy of 12, I was thrilled to see that it was possible to find out truth by reasoning alone... I became more and more convinced that nature could be understood as a relatively simple mathematical structure."

The mystery of the stars led Einstein to some of his greatest discoveries

J.J Grandville's "L'Autre Monde"

Switzerland

The move south

In the fall of 1894, circumstances led the 15-year-old Albert Einstein to relocate to **Switzerland**. His father's electrical business had gone bust, forcing the family to move their home to Italy where they believed there might be richer pickings. The plan was for Albert to stay in Munich to complete his schooling at Luitpold Gymnasium. But he was unhappy remaining there on his own. This, together with the school's dislike of Einstein's **rebellious attitude**, prompted him to leave. His intention was to enroll at Zurich Polytechnic to study math and physics, two years early. But there was another reason Einstein left Germany before turning 17: to dodge the draft. All German men were required to serve for a time in the army, a prospect that filled the authority-loathing Einstein with dread.

3-second Brief

Einstein moves to Switzerland where he finds education, social enlightenment, and love—and looks forward to spending his youth without the drudgery of national service.

School in Aarau

Einstein's plans to join Zurich Polytechnic in 1895 were scotched when he flunked his entrance exam. Although he passed the science sections of the test with flying colors, he fared less well in the general paper which included questions on everything from literature to foreign languages—subjects Einstein cared little for and so rarely studied. He resolved to try again the following year. In the interim, not wanting to return to Germany, he attended a school in the Swiss village of **Aarau**, 25 miles (40km) west of Zurich. The style of teaching there was much more liberal than he had experienced in Germany, encouraging **free thought** and **individualism** rather than conformity and rote learning. It was an approach that resonated strongly with Einstein. He finished with the second-best score in his class.

Related Thoughts

see also
ZURICH POLYTECHNIC
page 28
THE ACTIVIST
page 54

The Wintelers

During his stay in Aarau, Einstein boarded with the **Winteler family**. Just as he had found an intellectual home in the learning environment of Aarau school, so he found an emotional home with the Wintelers. They shared many of Einstein's liberal and **socialist instincts**, which the father of the family, Jost, helped Einstein cultivate into the values he would champion in later life. With the Wintelers Einstein grew socially, often spending evenings chatting with them rather than immersing himself in study as had been his habit in the past. After a few months spent lodging with the family, one of their daughters, **Marie**, became Albert's first girlfriend—the first of many it would turn out. Einstein's sister, Maja, would later marry the Wintelers' son, Paul.

"The only thing that interferes with my learning is my education."

Swiss Alps

Zurich Polytechnic

The freshman

In 1896, Albert Einstein retook his entrance exams to **Zurich Polytechnic**, scoring 5.5 out of a possible 6. He was in. Einstein was to train as a teacher specializing in math and physics. But Einstein's independence and original thinking began to land him in trouble. While he excelled at the theoretical aspects of his course—studying thermodynamics or the electromagnetic theory of **James Clerk Maxwell**—he rarely attended his practical classes. When he did, he would often disregard the instructions he was meant to follow and adopt his own methodology, much to the chagrin of his tutor, Professor Jean Pernet. Things came to a head when on one occasion Einstein's experimental ad-libbing caused an **explosion**, injuring his hand.

3-second Brief

Einstein enrolls as a physics student at Zurich Polytechnic. He soon proves himself to be a brilliant physicist, but a lazy and rebellious student.

Lazy dog!

It didn't take long for Einstein's lecturers in Zurich to begin tarring him with the same brush that had been well-used by his teachers in Munich. When he had initially failed the polytechnic's entrance exams in 1895, the head of the physics department, **Heinrich Weber**, had invited Einstein to stay in Zurich and attend the department's lectures despite not being enrolled there as a full-time student. Einstein declined. And it wasn't long before his contrarian attitude had damaged relations between the two men even further. "You're a very clever boy, Einstein," fumed Weber. "But you have one great fault: you won't let yourself be told anything." The most acerbic remark was meted out by Einstein's math professor, **Hermann Minkowski**, who branded him a **"lazy dog."** Minkowski would later eat his words when he became a great admirer of, and contributor to, the theory of relativity.

Related Thoughts

see also
ELECTROMAGNETISM
page 72
FOUNDATIONS OF THE SPECIAL THEORY
page 74

Graduation

Einstein graduated from Zurich in 1900, finishing fourth in his class—out of five. His dislike of experimental physics undoubtedly played a part in his lowly position, as did his dislike of more or less anything that didn't pique his interest. Part of the final mark was awarded for a research paper. For this, Einstein had wanted to investigate how the Earth moved through the **"ether"**—a substance through which **light waves** were once believed to propagate, rather like waves on the surface of a pond. But Weber was not impressed. So instead Einstein submitted a paper on heat, which he himself admitted was of no interest. All things considered, he should perhaps be thankful that he even graduated.

"Long live impudence! It is my guardian angel in this world."

James Clerk Maxwell

Zurich Polytechnic

Einstein in Love

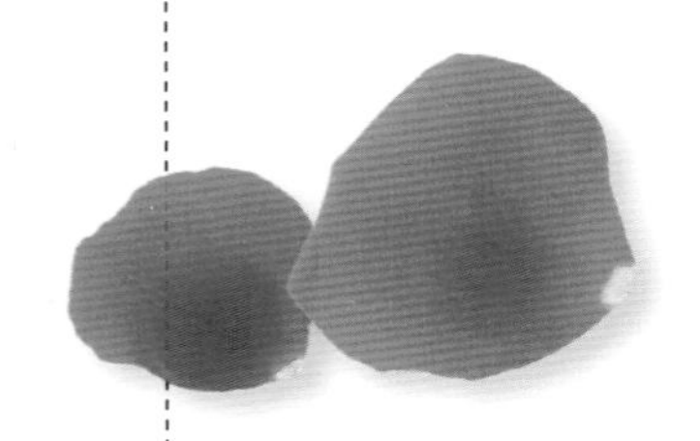

Mileva Maric

The person who finished fifth in Einstein's class at Zurich Polytechnic was a young woman named **Mileva Maric**—for the two years prior to their graduation, she and Einstein had been lovers. Maric was of Hungarian descent and nearly four years Albert's senior. She shared Einstein's **passion for science** and possessed an air of mystique that he found irresistible. The couple were married in Bern in 1903 and Maric became the mother of all three of Einstein's children. Ultimately, however, the great man's preoccupation with his work—and with other women—became too much for her to bear. They separated in 1914, and finally divorced in 1919. Mileva Maric died in 1948.

3-second Brief

Men of science, not troubled by their biological urges—that was the image of many scientists during the early twentieth century. But not Einstein.

Elsa Lowenthal

The final straw for Einstein's marriage to Mileva Maric was his relationship with **Elsa Lowenthal**. She was Einstein's cousin in two respects—her mother and Albert's mother were sisters, and their fathers were first cousins. Einstein had known Elsa when they were children, but his **involvement** with her didn't begin until 1912 during a visit to Berlin where she lived. Following his break-up with Maric in 1914, they moved in together. In contrast to the mysterious intellectual that was Maric, Elsa had little interest in science and cut a somewhat matronly figure. She was the strong **guardian and carer** that Einstein, now exhausted by work and the other pressures of life, needed to look after him. They were married in 1919.

Related Thoughts

see also
BERN
page 32
EINSTEIN'S CHILDREN
page 34

Cosmic womanizer

Einstein had **innumerable affairs** throughout his life. Women seemed to find his witty genius and striking looks **magnetically attractive**. And Einstein seemed more than happy to play along: "The upper half plans and thinks while the lower half determines our fate," he once wrote. His conquests included women from all walks of life. Even when he married Elsa, it was not before considering the hand of her 20-year-old daughter Ilse instead. The irrepressible Einstein didn't stop there, becoming romantically involved with his secretary **Betty Neumann**—apparently with Elsa's consent. Although generally charming and kind, if a little selfish, Einstein's attitude to women did occasionally lean toward the chauvinistic—such as the time he decided his son's fiancée wasn't attractive enough, and berated him for making such a poor choice.

"Any man who can drive safely while kissing a pretty girl is simply not giving the kiss the attention it deserves."

С.С.С.Р
Москва.
Главный Почтамт
До востребования
Маргарите Ивановне
Коненковой.
VIA AIR MAIL
U.S.S.R
Moscow.

Bern

The patent office

After graduating from Zurich Polytechnic in 1900, Einstein spent two **fruitless** years trying to secure an academic job. His search was hampered by two things. Firstly, his field—theoretical physics—was still an emerging discipline with few openings. Second, and more seriously, Einstein's **contrarianism** had made it all but impossible to get a good reference from any of his past professors at Zurich. In 1902, he gave up and took a job at the **Swiss patent office** in **Bern**, which he obtained through his friend Marcel Grossman, whose father knew the director. As "Technical Expert Third Class," it was Einstein's job to assess the technical merits of each application received. Einstein enjoyed the diversity of the work, and the money it brought in allowed him to marry his sweetheart Mileva Maric.

The Olympia Academy

While living in Bern, Einstein and two friends—Maurice Solovine and Conrad Habicht—formed a club that would meet regularly to discuss science and philosophy. They named themselves the **Olympia Academy**, lampooning the overblown titles sometimes given to learned societies. Among the works discussed by the academy were the writings of philosopher **David Hume** and mathematician **Henri Poincaré**. Although the club itself was short-lived, as both Solovine and Habicht left Bern within a couple of years, the trio remained lifelong friends.

Miracle year

Einstein continued to pursue his scientific research in his spare time. In 1905 his efforts came to fruition, propelling his name onto the international scientific stage. In that single year Einstein published four scientific papers, each one revolutionary. Firstly, he used the emerging field of quantum theory to explain the **photoelectric effect** (how some metals generate electricity when exposed to light). Next he turned his attention to **Brownian motion**, the seemingly random movements of particles suspended in the air—Einstein attributed this motion to collisions with atoms, proving the existence of these hitherto contentious particles. In the final two papers he laid out his **special theory of relativity**—the first paper rewrote the book on the motion of fast-moving objects and the second put forward his famous equation **$E=mc^2$**. No wonder that 1905 is regarded as Einstein's "miracle year."

3-second Brief

Unable to find employment at a university, Einstein accepts a job at the Swiss patent office in Bern. It leaves plenty of time for his true calling in science research.

Related Thoughts

see also
ELECTROMAGNETISM
page 72
THE SPECIAL THEORY OF RELATIVITY
page 76
STATISTICAL MECHANICS
page 94

"I was able to do a full day's work in only two or three hours. The remaining part of the day I would work out my own ideas."

Bern, Switzerland

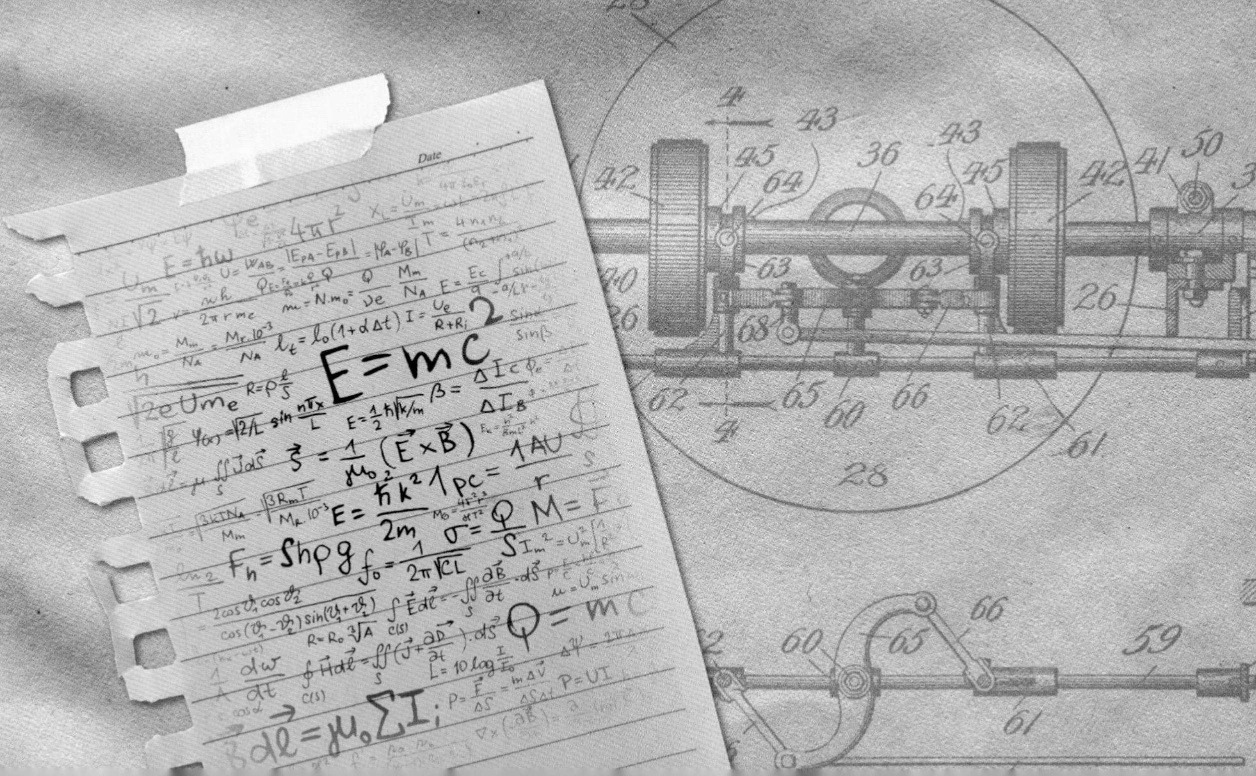

Einstein's Children

Hans Albert

Hans Albert Einstein was born on May 14, 1904, to Albert Einstein and his first wife, Mileva Maric. Einstein was thrilled and put his technical creativity to work designing toys for the baby, including a cable car made from **matchboxes and string**. But the relationship between father and son was often **strained**. During the break-up of his parents' marriage, Hans Albert became resentful toward Einstein. And when at age 15 Hans Albert announced his intention to train as an engineer, Einstein was furious—it was the profession that had driven his uncle and father to the brink of financial ruin through their electrical business. Hans Albert ultimately became Professor of Engineering at the University of California, Berkeley. He died in 1973 from heart failure, leaving three children.

Eduard

Eduard "Tete" Einstein was Albert and Mileva's second son, born in 1910. As with Hans Albert, Einstein was an attentive father during the child's early years but his relationship with Eduard deteriorated as the boy grew older, and they rarely saw one another after Einstein and Mileva had separated. Eduard attended Zurich University to study medicine, with ambitions of becoming a **psychiatrist**. But in a cruel irony he was struck down with the severe mental illness **schizophrenia** and spent much of his life in mental institutions, where it's now believed the primitive treatments probably made his condition worse. He died of a stroke in 1965 having never married, nor fathered any children.

Lieserl

Albert Einstein and Mileva Maric had a third child together—a daughter, named **Lieserl**. She was born in 1902, before both Hans Albert and Eduard. At the time, Einstein and Mileva did not yet have the means to get married. Einstein was living in Bern and about to start work in the patent office and it would have been difficult for him to reconcile an illegitimate child with a career as a respectable civil servant. Therefore Lieserl's existence was kept **secret**. It was only revealed when a collection of hitherto unknown letters between Einstein and Mileva were discovered in 1986. Her fate is still unknown. Some historians believe she was given up for adoption; others say she died of scarlet fever (letters between Maric and Einstein certainly indicate that she had contracted the disease). It's one **mystery** of Einstein's life that it's unlikely will ever be fully explained.

3-second Brief

Albert Einstein had three children—two sons, Hans Albert and Eduard, and also a daughter, Lieserl, whose existence historians only discovered 30 years after his death.

Related Thoughts

see also
EINSTEIN IN LOVE
page 30

"I have also considered many scientific plans during my pushing you around in your pram!"

Hans Albert
Eduard
Mileva Maric

The Rising Star

Professor Einstein

Despite publishing **four ground-breaking papers** in 1905, his "miracle year"—including his papers on the special theory of relativity—it was another three years before Einstein was finally able to get the academic job he so desired. In 1908, he secured a position as a lecturer at the **University of Bern**, although the salary and hours were insufficient to allow him to quit the patent office. Lecturing was the apprenticeship to becoming a full-time professor, though Einstein's lectures were poorly prepared and their delivery **shambolic**. Nevertheless, he persevered and in 1909 he finally realized his dream, being made Professor of Theoretical Physics at the University of Zurich.

To Prague

Physics departments at other universities were beginning to notice, and indeed covet, the celebrated talents of **Professor Einstein**. So much so that, in 1910, he was head-hunted for a professorial place at the prestigious **Karl-Ferdinand University** in Prague. He duly accepted and took up the position in 1911. Zurich didn't let him go without a fight though, offering to raise his salary by more than 20 percent. It was while in Prague that Einstein began to take considerable strides from the special theory of relativity toward his broader, but vastly more complex, general theory of relativity, working out how the theory predicted that light should be bent in a gravitational field. Einstein's renown meanwhile continued to grow, with him receiving **invitations to lecture** at universities and conferences across Europe.

...and then Berlin

In 1912, Einstein moved from Prague back to Zurich to take up a position at his old polytechnic, which had recently been upgraded to become the **Swiss Federal Institute of Technology**. But the big breakthrough came when he was offered a professorship at the **University of Berlin**, at that time the world's premier scientific institute. In addition, he would be made Director of Berlin's new Kaiser Wilhelm Institute for Physics and be admitted to the Prussian Academy of Sciences—becoming its youngest member at age 34. Better still, he would have minimal teaching duties, allowing him to dedicate the bulk of his time to research. Einstein accepted and took up the appointment in 1914. It was a decision that paid off—a year later, he published his magnum opus: the **general theory of relativity**.

3-second Brief

Even after the special theory of relativity, it takes Einstein another three years to get an academic job. But then his career launches into the stratosphere.

Related Thoughts

see also
BERN
page 32
FOUNDATIONS OF THE GENERAL THEORY
page 80
THE GENERAL THEORY OF RELATIVITY
page 82

"I've been so deluged with questions, invitations, and requests that I dream I'm burning in Hell and the postman is the Devil eternally roaring at me, hurling new bundles of letters at my head."

University of Berlin

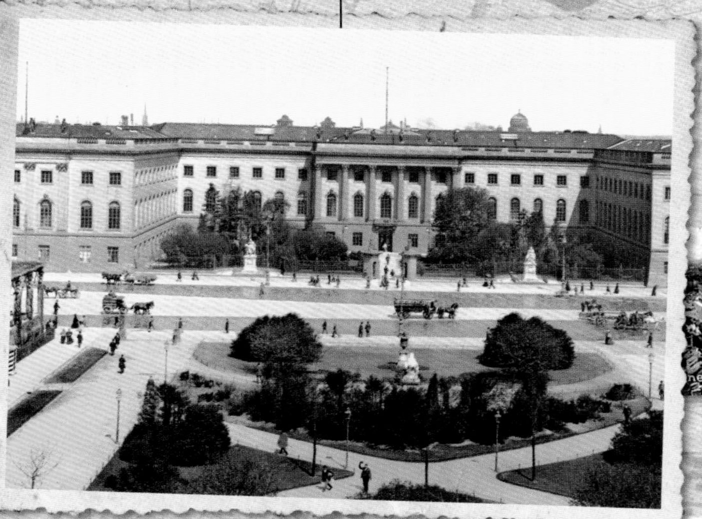

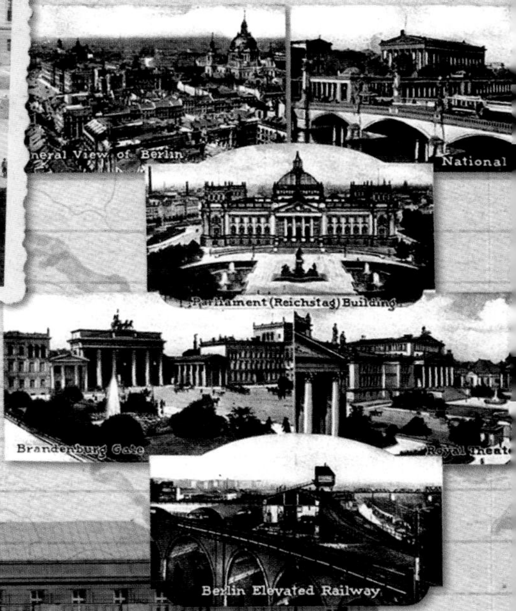
neral View of Berlin
National
Parliament (Reichstag) Building
Brandenburg Gate
Royal Theat
Berlin Elevated Railway

Karl-Ferdinand
University, Prague

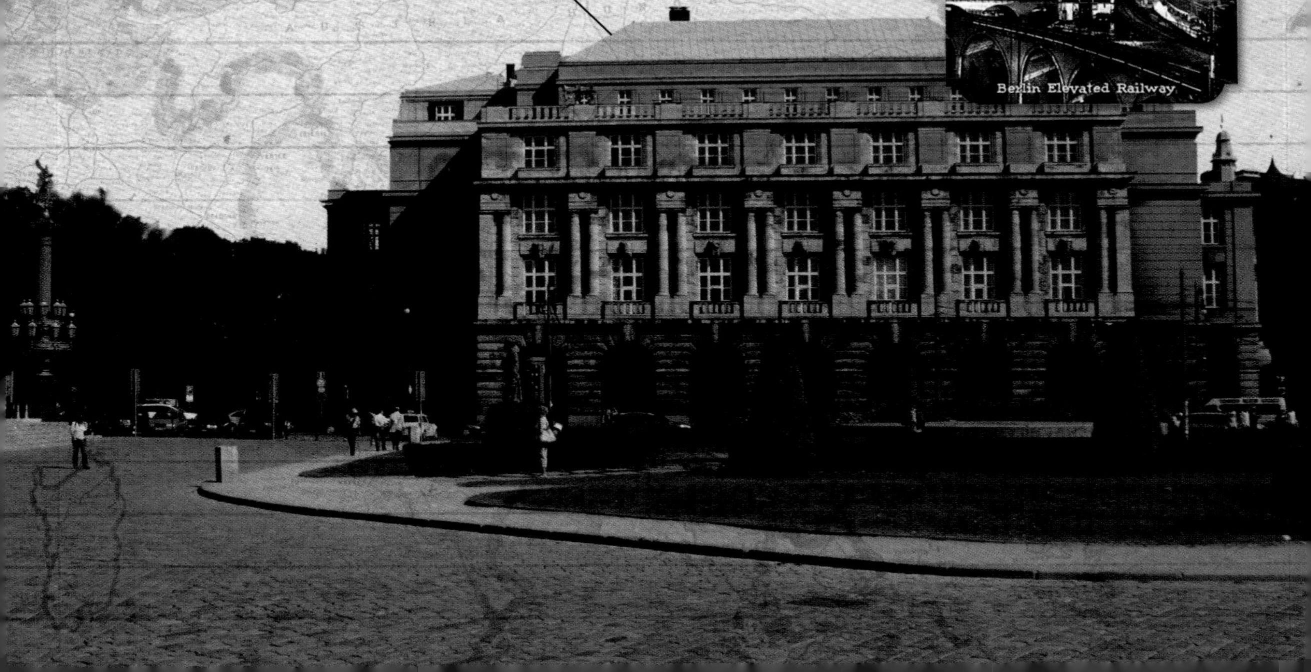

The Reluctant Celebrity

A household name

Following the publication of his general theory of relativity—and especially after the experimental verification of its light-bending predictions by English astrophysicist **Arthur Eddington**—Albert Einstein became renowned not just in scientific circles, but as a celebrity the world over. The press loved him: in one man they found a **scientific genius** who could furnish them with fascinating stories about the Universe, and a **photogenic rebel** with a sharp wit who seldom failed to deliver a pithy quote in response to their questions. Accordingly the public was captivated. Einstein claimed to find all the media interest extremely tiresome but many of those close to him believed otherwise—that the performer in him secretly enjoyed their clamoring attentions.

Einstein-mania

In 1921, more than 40 years before The Beatles would whip the public into a frenzy at live performances during their second tour of the United States, Albert Einstein embarked upon his own **US tour**—and the reception he received was scarcely less fanatical. He began in New York and then took in Washington D.C., Chicago, Princeton, Harvard, Hartford, and Cleveland. In New York, Einstein was driven through the streets in a motorcade, amid blaring horns and cheering crowds. In Washington he visited the White House, meeting **President Warren G. Harding**. Meanwhile, his lectures were **sold out**—despite the fact that he was speaking in German.

The red carpet

Einstein's **fame** was here to stay. In 1921 he had visited the United States' East Coast and Midwest regions, but in 1931 he returned to visit the West Coast. He spent time at the California Institute of Technology, one of America's finest science research centers, and visited Mt. Wilson Observatory at the time when astronomers were discovering the expansion of the Universe. During a tour of Hollywood he met and became friends with the actor **Charlie Chaplin**, with whom he shared strong **left-wing** political sentiments. Chaplin, Einstein, and his second wife Elsa famously attended the premiere of Chaplin's film *City Lights* together, enjoying a rapturous greeting from the crowd, which prompted Chaplin to remark: "They cheer me because they all understand me, and they cheer you because no-one understands you." During the visit Elsa charged members of the public $1 for autographs and $5 for photographs—the proceeds all going to children's charities.

3-second Brief

Einstein's name spreads around the globe and Einstein-mania grips the USA. Meanwhile, Einstein himself pays a visit to the President and goes to the movies with Charlie Chaplin.

Related Thoughts

see also
WHO WAS ALBERT EINSTEIN?
page 46
POPULAR INFLUENCE
page 144

"With fame I become more and more stupid, which of course is a very common phenomenon."

Einstein and Charlie Chaplin, 1931

President Warren G. Harding

The Nobel Prize

For services to physics

Einstein received the **1921 Nobel Prize in Physics** for his work on the photoelectric effect and for "services to theoretical physics." The mystery was why it had taken so long for the greatest physicist of his generation to win this, the greatest accolade in physics. Einstein was passed over for the prize in 1920 owing to the huge surge in publicity following the confirmation of his general theory of relativity, which led many to view him as a **self-promoter**. In 1921, amazingly, the Nobel committee chose to award no prize rather than recognize Einstein. It was only in 1922 that it saw fit to award him the 1921 prize retrospectively (while giving the 1922 prize itself to Danish quantum physicist **Niels Bohr**). Einstein's reaction was typically Einstein—choosing to visit Japan rather than accept the award in person.

Swedish alimony

Einstein always expected that one day he would win the Nobel Prize, so much so that, during his divorce negotiations with Mileva in 1918, he included an offer to give her the entire sum of any future Nobel Prize money. For the 1921 prize this came to **121,572 Swedish krona**, or $32,250—equivalent to nearly $400,000 today. Whether he actually honored his promise though is a point hotly debated by historians. Evidence uncovered in 2006 suggests that Einstein instead **invested** a good deal of the money—and consequently **lost** most of it in the economic upheaval of the Great Depression.

Relativity's greatest paradox

Einstein's 1921 Nobel Prize—for the **photoelectric effect** and the perhaps deliberately obscure "services to theoretical physics"—was the only time he received the award. Perhaps one of the **greatest injustices** in science is that the Nobel Committee never recognized his theory of relativity, which (alongside quantum theory) turned out to be one of the two great pillars of twentieth-century physics. Einstein had been nominated for his 1905 special theory of relativity on many occasions between 1910 and 1922, but failed to win, because the theory was so radical, the committee claimed that the evidence to support it was so meager. Posthumous nominations are not permitted, so it seems there will now never be a Nobel Prize for what was the **greatest achievement** of Albert Einstein's mind.

3-second Brief

In 1921, Einstein finally receives the Nobel Prize in Physics—16 years after publishing his theory of relativity. He was so thrilled that he went to Japan rather than accept it in person.

Related Thoughts

see also
ELECTROMAGNETISM
page 72
THE SPECIAL THEORY OF RELATIVITY
page 76

"To punish me for my contempt of authority, Fate has made me an authority myself."

Commemorative Einstein stamps

Nobel Prize Medal

Other Honors

The Copley Medal

Einstein was showered with many other scientific **accolades** besides the Nobel Prize. In 1925, he received the Copley Medal from London's Royal Society. Named in honor of **Sir Godfrey Copley**, who provided the Royal Society with funding for the award in 1709, it predates the Nobel Prize by nearly 200 years. It was a refreshing change to be given an award by an English institution. He had received notice in 1920 that he was to receive the Gold Medal of the Royal Astronomical Society (RAS)—until, that is, a group of bigoted members protested about the prize going to a German-Swiss-Jew, and it was consequently **withheld**. They later changed their minds though, and Einstein received the RAS Gold Medal in 1926.

The Max Planck Medal

In 1929, Einstein received the inaugural **Max Planck Medal** from the German Physical Society, for excellence in theoretical physics. It was presented to him by physicist Planck himself, Einstein's friend and colleague for many years. The medal was one of a deluge of prizes and honors that Einstein had received since Eddington's confirmation of the general theory of relativity had propelled him to **stardom**, including no less than **five honorary doctorates**. While Einstein readily accepted his plaudits, he viewed this and other awards as matters of little significance compared to the satisfaction he derived from his work.

Person of the century

On June 14, 1999—44 years after his death—Albert Einstein appeared on the front cover of *Time* magazine. The reason: he had **topped** the magazine's list of the 100 most influential people of the twentieth century, beating the likes of Mother Teresa, Mahatma Gandhi, and Bill Gates. *Time's* editors cited the fact that the century "will be remembered foremost for its science and technology," for which Einstein was the **natural icon**. Einstein had already made the cover of *Time* on four previous occasions. The February 18, 1929 issue carried a piece on his quest for a unified field theory. April 4, 1938 featured a report on his escape to Princeton following his flight from Nazi Germany. An issue from July 1, 1946 contemplated the legacy of the atomic bomb. And the February 19, 1979 edition carried a cover story to commemorate the centenary of Einstein's birth. While few disputed Einstein's coronation as "**person of the century**," the list was controversial for its inclusion of Adolf Hitler and cartoon character Bart Simpson.

3-second Brief

Following the Nobel Prize, accolades begin to pour in—culminating in *Time* magazine's Person of the Century award, narrowly beating Mother Teresa and Bart Simpson.

Related Thoughts

see also
EPONYMOUS DISCOVERIES
page 140
CULTURAL LEGACY
page 148

"The value of achievement lies in the achieving."

Max Planck

בנק ישראל
5
חמש לירות
ישראליות
יושב ראש
המועצה המייעצת
נגיד הבנק
1968

PRINCETON, NJ
MAR
14
1966
08540
Prominent American
Series
ALBERT EINSTEIN
MATHEMATICIAN-PHYSICIST
NOBEL PRIZE WINNER
1879–1955
8c
Artmaster
First Day of Issue

A Beautiful Mind

Brain power

Just how **clever** was Albert Einstein? We'll never know for sure because he never took a formal intelligence test. But scientists have tried to estimate his **IQ**, based on what is known about him. The IQ scale works by classifying a person's mental prowess using a single number representing their mental age, divided by their true age, multiplied by 100. IQ is a general measure of intelligence, and although Einstein excelled at math and physics that is no guarantee that he would demonstrate the same level of ability in other areas, such as language skills—indeed, Einstein failed his first entrance exam to Zurich Polytechnic for that very reason. Nevertheless, Einstein's IQ estimate came in at **over 160**, placing his mental prowess in the top 0.003 percent of the population.

3-second Brief

Albert Einstein would doubtless have breezed through the Mensa entrance exam, and had powers of concentration that enabled him to work through all but the loudest din.

Recipe for genius

It wasn't just an intellectual powerhouse that drove Einstein to his astonishing achievements. Inside his brain was a **potent cocktail** of other talents and abilities that facilitated the mental leaps others found impossible. His imagination and creativity led him to consider solutions to problems that simply had not occurred to other scientists. His **single-mindedness** and capacity for hard work meant there was no stopping Einstein once he got the bit between his teeth. For example, he worked close to the point of exhaustion during the formulation of his general theory of relativity. And his legendary **powers of concentration** enabled him to block out all but the loudest distractions. On one occasion, at a dinner held in his honor, he was so absorbed in scribbling equations under the table that he completely missed his cue to get up and speak—despite a standing ovation.

Related Thoughts

see also
ZURICH POLYTECHNIC
page 28
THE GENERAL THEORY OF RELATIVITY
page 82

The geek syndrome

In 2003, scientists from the universities of Oxford and Cambridge announced studies suggesting that Einstein may have suffered from a mild form of autism, known as **Asperger syndrome**. The condition is named after Austrian pediatrician Hans Asperger, who in the 1940s noticed a characteristic set of traits in some children: narrow interests intensely pursued, to the point of obsession, coupled with diminished empathy and communication skills. The 2003 researchers cited as evidence Einstein's difficulty in relationships, his **obsession** with his work, and his childhood habit of repeating sentences over and over. Today, the condition is thought to manifest itself in the brains of many who excel at math, science, or computing, leading some to call it the "**geek syndrome**."

"I have no special talents. I am only passionately curious."

Who was Albert Einstein?

Random acts of kindness

It wasn't just a quick wit and a head for figures that shaped Albert Einstein. Among his many endearing personal qualities was his **kindness**. During his latter years in America, he frequently tutored local school children in math and science—free of charge. He once granted an interview to a struggling journalism student whose teacher had promised him a top grade if he bagged an interview with the world's greatest scientist. Paradoxically though, Einstein's kindness seemed to run out when it came to members of his own family. Einstein craved his **independence**. When that was compromised by the emotional demands of his loved ones, he would often retreat into his work, making him appear a cold husband and a somewhat **distant father**.

3-second Brief

He's been variously described as a rebel, an eccentric, and the embodiment of human kindness—yet the real Albert Einstein was an even stranger mix still.

The eccentric

Einstein has become the blueprint for the **wild-haired**, absent-minded professor. Once, while out in the rain, Einstein removed his hat, explaining: "My hair has withstood water many times before, but I don't know how many times my hat can." His sense of direction was hopeless and he would frequently get lost while out walking, on one occasion phoning his departmental secretary to ask where his house was. The same **bumbling distractedness** proved to be a dangerous mix when he was enjoying his favorite hobby—sailing—and he often had to be rescued by members of his yacht club. As if to top it all, he never wore socks, even on formal occasions—disguising the fact by wearing high boots. Einstein was the archetypal **eccentric**, and he was loved for it.

Related Thoughts

see also
EINSTEIN'S CHILDREN
page 34
THE EVIDENCE FOR RELATVITY
page 88

Brass neck

For someone who in most respects was so humble and easy-going, Einstein was prone to monumental displays of **arrogance** and **cheek**. In 1901, after reading a paper describing the properties of metals in terms of subatomic particles called electrons, he wrote to its author, Professor Paul Drude at Germany's Giessen University, poking several holes in his arguments—and then promptly asking for a job. When Drude penned a less-than-appreciative response, Einstein vowed to destroy him in the research journals. He was equally **dismissive** in defending his own theories against critics. When a journalist asked him what he would have done if astronomer Arthur Eddington's eclipse observations had been at odds with the theory of relativity, Einstein replied: "Then I would feel sorry for the good Lord. The theory is correct."

"The ideals which have lighted my way, and time after time have given me new courage to face life cheerfully, have been Kindness, Beauty, and Truth."

Einstein lecture, 1940

Religion

Lost Jew

Like most other things in Albert Einstein's life, his relationship with religion was characteristically **unconventional**. He was born into a Jewish family, who cared little for the Jewish faith or way of life—so much so that they sent him to a Catholic rather than a Jewish school. There, he greatly enjoyed learning about the **Catholic faith**—even to the point of helping other students with their work. When Einstein moved up to high school, he received his first formal tuition in **Judaism**. He took great interest in these studies and was inspired to observe the customs of the Jewish religion—possibly an early manifestation of his rebellious streak, kicking back against his parents' religious indifference.

The ephemeral atheist

Einstein's enthusiasm for Judaism was soon eclipsed by his passion for a new religion: **science**. At high school, and in his private life, Einstein began fervently digesting the writings of the great scientists and philosophers. And these works of **rationalism** instilled in Einstein a sense that he had been cheated and lied to by the Bible. Although this aversion to the formalities of organized religion lodged with Einstein for the rest of his life, he later denied outright disbelief in God, finding a new faith in the **beauty and order of nature**. Indeed, he publicly derided the atheism of others as nothing more than a form of bigotry.

Spinoza's God

Rather than subscribing to the notion of a bearded man on a cloud, dispensing rewards and punishments for the good and evil deeds of humanity, Einstein came round to the idea of a God manifested in the **harmony of nature**. It was a view that had been put forward by the seventeenth-century Dutch philosopher **Baruch Spinoza**. "I believe in Spinoza's God, who reveals Himself in the lawful harmony of the world," said Einstein in 1929, "not in a God Who concerns Himself with the fate and the doings of mankind." This philosophy even influenced Einstein's scientific work—he once stated that when assessing the merits of a scientific theory he would sometimes ask himself whether **God** would have designed things that way.

3-second Brief

You'd think the man who tackled the mysteries of space and time with his bare hands might have little time for the uncertainties of religion. Far from it.

Related Thoughts

see also
THE ACTIVIST
page 54

"Science without religion is lame. Religion without science is blind."

President Franklin D. Roosevelt

The Activist

Zionism

During the early decades of the twentieth century, Einstein was sympathetic to the cause of **Zionist Jews**, who were calling for the establishment of a homeland for the Jewish people. Einstein became such a supporter of Zionism that his visit to the United States in 1921 was partly to use his **growing celebrity** to help raise capital there for the cause. However, his enthusiasm for Zionism subsequently waned. Einstein's aversion to nationalism eventually led him to question whether turning the Jews into a **nationalistic** people was really a good idea—and whether it might bring them more trouble than it was worth. He also criticized Britain's handling of the creation of the State of Israel, when it finally came about in 1948.

World peace

Einstein once described himself as a **militant pacifist**—prepared to fight for peace. In fact, he even urged young men to defy the laws of their countries and not participate in military service, stating: "Nothing will end war unless the people themselves refuse to go to war." That view became less absolute as Einstein got older, with the growing realization that military action was the only way to stop Adolf Hitler. But it never disappeared. After the atomic bombs were dropped on Japan at the end of the war, Einstein regretted writing the letter to Roosevelt that led to the development of the US **A-bomb**, stating that he only did it out of fear that the Germans would develop a working bomb first. He dedicated much time in his later years to the **peace movement**—for example, founding the Emergency Committee of Atomic Scientists to campaign for nuclear arms control.

Racial tolerance

Einstein believed passionately that the breaking down of national barriers—and the appointment of a **single world government**—was the only sure path to lasting global peace. That, paired with his own experiences of anti-Semitism as a Jew, fostered in Einstein a strong belief in the equality of all races. During his time living at Princeton he became a vociferous **critic of racial discrimination** in the United States, joining the National Association for the Advancement of Colored People (NAACP) and campaigning hard for the civil liberties of African Americans. He branded racism "America's worst disease."

3-second Brief

Einstein was a fierce objector to the power of coercion throughout his life—from encouraging draft dodgers in Europe to fighting racism in 1950s America.

Related Thoughts

see also
THE WAR YEARS
page 52
CULTURAL LEGACY
page 148

"*Never do anything against conscience even if the state demands it.*"

Einstein and wife with proponents of Zionism aboard the *SS Rotterdam*

Political Science

Social democrat

Einstein's sense of fairness and his loathing of class divisions gave him decidedly **left-wing** political tendencies. Yet he had little time for Soviet-style authoritarianism. Einstein's socialism was tinged with a respect for personal freedom, free speech, and individualism—he was a **social democrat**. These latent beliefs had been cultivated in Einstein's mind by early discussions with Jost Winteler, the father of the family with whom he had boarded during his time at Aarau school, just prior to enrolling at Zurich Polytechnic. And they stayed with him for life. Despite being a good lefty though, Einstein believed that establishing **world peace** was more important than the particular political model of any one nation. He also shunned allegiance to any one political party, believing it to be a symptom of lazy thinking.

President Einstein

In 1952, Einstein was given the opportunity to put his political ideals into practice. When Chaim Weizmann, Israel's first president, died in 1952, the country's prime minister, **David Ben-Gurion**, gave in to public pressure and asked Einstein if he would consider the position. Einstein, however, declined—claiming he possessed neither the people skills, nor the tact or ability as a manager, to see the job through. Indeed, these were demands that sat very awkwardly with Einstein's own rebellious instincts. Einstein declared he was a **scientist first**, not a politician: "Politics is for the present, while our equations are for eternity." By all accounts, Ben-Gurion was quite relieved to hear this.

The Red Scare

Following the Second World War, fear grew in the United States of the threat posed by **communism**. Rivalry between the United States and the Soviet Union had led to the division of postwar Germany into two states—East and West. Meanwhile, the Soviet Union developed its own nuclear capability and a number of US officials admitted to being Soviet spies. There followed a communist witch hunt in the United States led by Wisconsin Senator **Joseph McCarthy**, with many outspoken socialists and intellectuals being investigated for possible communist connections. Einstein was among them. In fact, the FBI had been collating a dossier on him since as far back as 1932. Einstein was highly critical of the **Red Scare**, as it became known, arguing that such an attack on civil liberties in the interests of "security" was as dangerous as communism itself.

3-second Brief

For a scientist, Einstein was very outspoken politically. During the early 1950s, his radical politics led the McCarthy inquisition to brand him a traitor and a spy.

Related Thoughts

see also
SWITZERLAND
page 26
THE ACTIVIST
page 54

"The only salvation for civilization and the human race lies in the creation of a world government."

Great Seal
of the
United States
Joseph McCarthy
E PLURIBUS UNUM

"It Is Time To Go"

Farewell, Albert

Einstein had suffered with stomach problems for much of his life. But in 1948 he was gripped by acute abdominal pain and was admitted to hospital. Surgeons there diagnosed him with an **aortic aneurysm**—a swelling of the major artery carrying blood to the abdomen. They warned that one day it would burst and probably kill him—and seven years later it did. He collapsed and was rushed to hospital. Doctors offered him surgery but Einstein knew the chances of success were slim and so declined, saying: "I have done my share, **it is time to go**. I will do it elegantly." Albert Einstein died in hospital a little after 1:00 a.m. on April 18, 1955. Next to his bed lay a draft of a speech that he was due to deliver on Israeli Independence Day and an unfinished unified field theory calculation. Science and humanism had remained his principal interests right up until the end.

3-second Brief

One of the greatest physicists who ever lived ends his days in a Princeton hospital bed aged 76, surrounded not by family and friends—but by mathematics.

Cremation

By the time newspaper headlines appeared announcing that Einstein had died, his body had already been cremated. In accordance with Einstein's specific instructions, it was a small ceremony exclusively for family and friends held on the afternoon of his death. His ashes were scattered soon after in the **Delaware River**. Before Einstein's body could be laid to rest, a routine postmortem was carried out. But, in an **extraordinary twist**, the pathologist, Thomas Harvey, removed Einstein's brain—doing so without the consent of his family. When later confronted about what he'd done, Harvey defended his actions, claiming that they had been in the interests of science and arguing that Einstein would have approved.

Related Thoughts

see also
POLITICAL SCIENCE
page 56
UNIFIED FIELD THEORY
page 100

What's in a brain?

Harvey sliced up Einstein's brain and made microscope slides from the pieces which he sent out to brain researchers, though few published results came of them. As if this **ghoulish act** were not enough, Harvey it seems then kept the brain in his personal possession for 43 years before finally returning it to the hospital. Of the few scientific studies that were carried out on the samples Harvey took, the most prominent was by neuroscientists at Canada's McMaster University. They found that Einstein had a shorter groove in his brain's **parietal lobe** than is usual—a feature believed to be connected to **mathematical ability**. That tidbit of information seems a paltry reward indeed for desecrating the mortal remains of one of the greatest scientists who ever lived.

"The fear of death is the most unjustified of all fears."

Einstein's study at Princeton University, 1955

Timeline

1879
Albert Einstein is born in the German city of Ulm, to parents Hermann and Pauline. His sister, Maja, is born two years later.

1894
Einstein moves to Switzerland in preparation to study math and physics at Zurich Polytechnic, and to avoid national service in the German Army.

1895
A bicycle ride inspires one of Einstein's most famous thought experiments—wondering what it might be like to ride alongside a light beam.

1902
Unable to secure an academic job, Einstein takes work at the Swiss patent office in Bern, continuing his scientific research in his spare time.

1904
Having married Mileva Maric in 1902, the Einsteins' son Hans Albert is born, followed six years later by the birth of Eduard.

1914
Einstein's growing renown lands him a professorship at the prestigious University of Berlin.

1921
Following the success of the general theory of relativity, Einstein embarks upon a sell-out lecturing tour of the US.

1922
Einstein retrospectively receives the 1921 Nobel Prize in Physics, though it's for his explanation of the photoelectric effect—not for his theory of relativity.

1931
Einstein leaves Germany for another three-month tour of America. But Hitler's rise to power and Einstein's Jewish roots mean he never returns.

1939
Einstein and Hungarian physicist Leó Szilárd realize the potential of nuclear fission to create the atomic bomb. Einstein writes to President Roosevelt warning him.

1940
Having been granted permanent residency in the United States in 1933 after escaping Nazi Germany, Einstein is finally sworn in as a US citizen.

1955
Einstein dies at Princeton Hospital from a burst aortic aneurysm. He is 76 years old.

1999
Time magazine makes Einstein Person of the Century, ahead of Mother Teresa and Mahatma Gandhi.

Glossary

Anti-Semitism Racial hatred directed toward Jews. Became widespread across Europe in the buildup to the Second World War.

Atheist Someone who rejects the existence of any form of deity and shuns religion.

Arthur Eddington British astronomer and astrophysicist who in 1919 confirmed Einstein's general theory of relativity by measuring light bending near the Sun.

Eduard Einstein Einstein's second son, born in 1910 and institutionalized for schizophrenia for much of his life. He died of a stroke in 1955.

Elsa Einstein Einstein's second wife. They married in 1919—the same year that he divorced Mileva Maric. She died in 1936.

Hans Albert Einstein Einstein's first son, born in 1904. Hans Albert became Professor of Engineering at the University of California. He died in 1973.

Lieserl Einstein The illegitimate daughter of Einstein and Mileva Maric. Born in 1902, her fate is unknown.

Maja Einstein Einstein's sister, born 1881. The two were extremely close, and Einstein was devastated when she died in 1951.

IAS The Institute for Advanced Studies in Princeton, New Jersey, where Einstein worked after fleeing Nazism in Europe.

Elsa Lowenthal Einstein's second wife, who was also his cousin. They were married in 1919. Elsa died in 1936.

Luitpold Gymnasium Einstein's high school in Munich, which he attended between 1888 and 1895.

Manhattan Project The Second World War project to build the American atomic bomb, culminating in the destruction of Hiroshima and Nagasaki.

Mileva Maric Einstein's first wife, whom he met while studying at Zurich Polytechnic. They were married in 1903, and divorced in 1919. Mileva died in 1948.

McCarthyism Senator Joseph McCarthy's attempted purge of communism in the United States. Einstein was investigated for his pacifism and socialist views.

Hermann Minkowski Einstein's math tutor at Zurich Polytechnic, who famously branded him a "lazy dog."

Miracle year In 1905, the publication of four landmark papers—the special theory, E=mc2, the photoelectric effect, and Brownian motion—put Einstein on the map as a physicist.

Olympia Academy The science discussion group formed by Einstein and friends Maurice Solovine and Conrad Habicht in Bern.

Pacifism Refusal to bear arms or to participate in, or support, violence and hostilities during times of war.

Parietal lobe Part of the brain positioned on top and to the rear, thought to play a role in numerical reasoning and spatial awareness.

Spinoza's God A deity, manifest in the harmony of the natural world, conceived by Dutch philosopher Baruch Spinoza.

Max Talmud A family friend of the Einsteins while Albert was still a child. He brought books to nurture the young genius's interest in science.

Zionism Movement for the creation of a Jewish homeland—Israel—formally established in 1948.

Zurich Polytechnic Institution where Einstein carried out his undergraduate studies. Now renamed the Swiss Federal Institute of Technology Zurich.

Einstein
USA 15c

Chapter 2

Theories

Structure of Matter

Capillary rise

Einstein's first scientific research paper was published in March 1901, in the journal *Annalen der Physik* (*Annals of Physics*). It concerned an effect known as "**capillary rise**." Stand a narrow tube upright in a beaker of water and the water will rise up the inside of the tube. Einstein attempted to explain the effect in terms of forces between the water molecules, which he tried to model as obeying a law similar to **Newton's law of gravity**. Alas, Einstein's theory was wrong. Although capillary action is caused by the forces between molecules (of both the liquid and the walls of the tube), the mathematical form of the force is very different to that described by Newton's gravitational theory. Nevertheless, the paper meant Einstein was now a **published physicist**.

3-second Brief

Einstein begins his scientific career by unpicking the properties of matter. No university would employ him so he was forced to carry out his research in his spare time.

The size of molecules

In July 1905, Einstein submitted his doctoral dissertation to the University of Zurich. In it, he derived a neat estimate of the size of molecules. Molecules are made by joining together atoms. For example, each molecule of water is made by joining together two atoms of **hydrogen** with an atom of **oxygen**. Einstein devised mathematical equations to model the viscosity—the stickiness—of a sugar-water solution. Then, using data on sugar-water viscosity obtained experimentally, he solved his equations, finding that a volume of 47.3 pints (22.4 liters) at 68°F (20°C) and standard atmospheric pressure contains 2.1×10^{23} molecules—a huge number equal to 21 followed by 22 zeroes. Today, the accepted value of this number (known as "**Avogadro's constant**") is 6.022×10^{23}. From this Einstein was able to deduce the size of each individual molecule.

Related Thoughts

see also
STATISTICAL MECHANICS
page 94
THE QUANTUM WORLD
page 96

Quantum vibrations

In 1906, Einstein constructed a theory of solid matter that took account of the new physics of **quantum mechanics**, which says that energy can only exist in indivisible discrete chunks. Einstein's theory modeled matter as a **three-dimensional lattice of atoms or molecules** linked together by springs (there aren't really any springs—it was just Einstein's way of visualizing the forces). Next, he assumed that because of quantum laws the springs are only allowed to vibrate at particular frequencies. His theory predicted that at low temperatures the vibrations of atoms should cease altogether, neatly explaining some anomalous **properties of solids** at low temperature that had been baffling experimental physicists for some time.

"Science is a wonderful thing if one does not have to earn one's living at it."

Molecules
Sir Isaac Newton
SIR ISAAC NEWTON

Nature of Light

Wave-particle duality

During 1905 Einstein published four **groundbreaking** papers, leading many to refer to this as his "miracle year." One of the papers provided the explanation for the photoelectric effect, whereby light falling on certain metals causes the metal to give off electrons. Einstein's explanation invoked an idea put forward in 1900 by German physicist **Max Planck** that light comes in discrete chunks. Planck had introduced the idea simply as a tool to help understand the interaction of radiation with matter—nothing more. But Einstein took it literally, arguing that light waves really are made up of particles. Planck, and most other physicists, hated the idea but it turned out to be right. **Particles of light** were observed experimentally by British physicist Arthur Compton in 1923, and later named "photons."

Stimulated emission

Einstein's theories underpin the operation of modern lasers. These work on a principle known as "stimulated emission," which he developed in 1917. Einstein drew upon a new **theory of the atom** which had been put forward by his colleague, the Danish physicist **Niels Bohr**. In Bohr's theory, electron particles orbit around the atom's central nucleus in a series of levels, each corresponding to different energies. When the atom absorbs a photon of light, it raises the energy level of an electron. And the reverse happens each time a photon is given off. Einstein tried to use Bohr's model to derive Planck's 1900 **theory of radiation**. But he found he was only able to do it if photons emitted by one atom can trigger the emission of identical photons by other atoms—and this is stimulated emission.

Stark-Einstein law

The **Stark-Einstein law** was derived independently by Einstein and the German physicist Johannes Stark during the early twentieth century. It essentially says that radiation causes physical and chemical changes in matter, and that each photon of radiation can affect at most one atom or molecule of matter. In other words, to bring about a change to a sample of N atoms of a substance using radiation you need to bombard it with at least N photons. This is why it's sometimes known as the "**photoequivalence law**." In honor of Einstein's contribution, his name was given to a unit of irradiance used in photochemistry. One "Einstein" is the number of photons equal to Avogadro's constant.

3-second Brief

Einstein's radical thinking overturns the applecart in the understanding of light and radiation. Ironically, Einstein's breakthroughs lay the foundations for quantum theory, which he later comes to detest.

Related Thoughts

see also
STRUCTURE OF MATTER
page 66
ELECTROMAGNETISM
page 72

"When a light ray is propagated from a point, the energy... consists of a finite number of energy quanta which are localized at points in space and which can be produced and absorbed only as complete units."

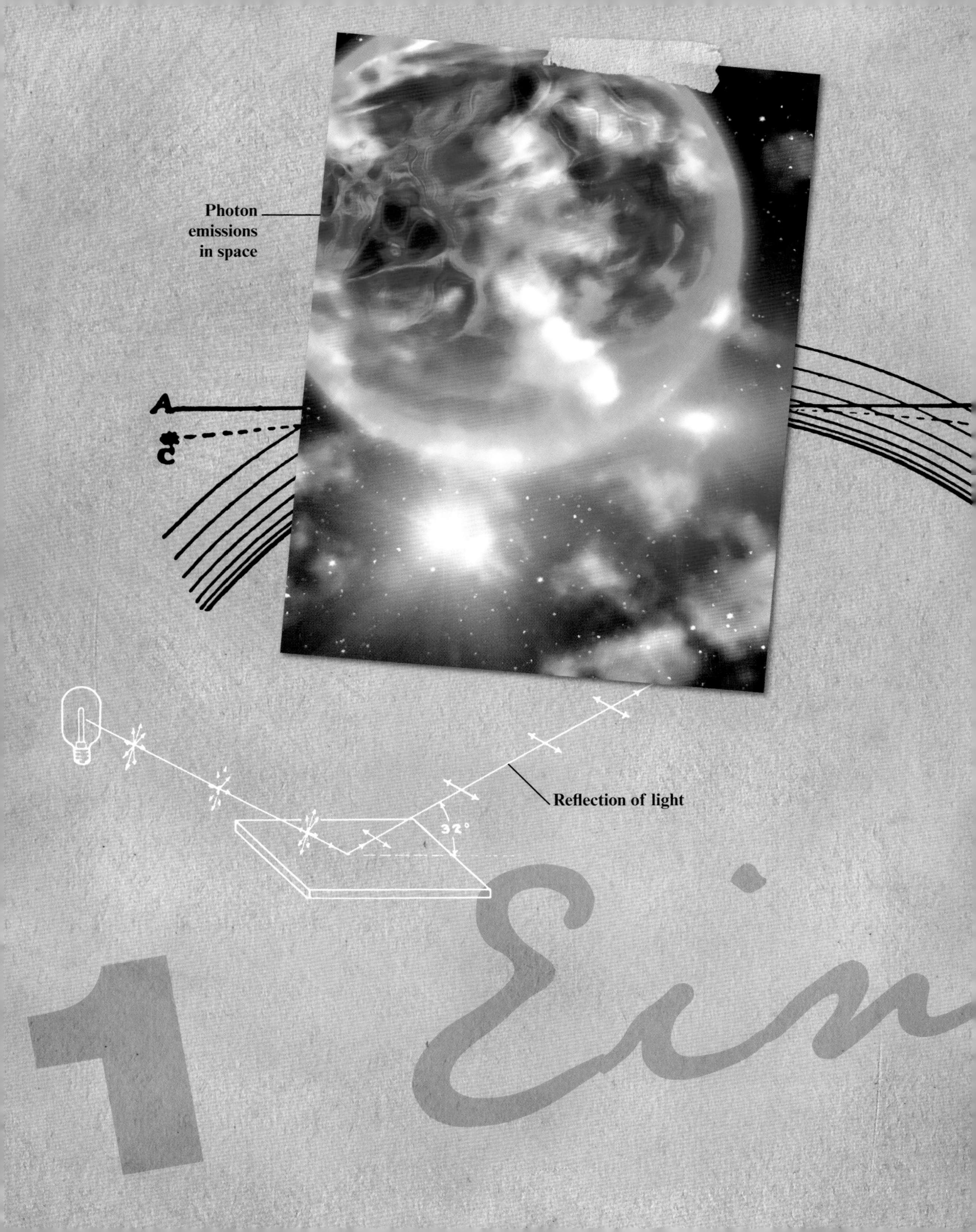
Photon
emissions
in space
A
C
32°
Reflection of light
1
Ein

Thermodynamics

The Einstein relation

Thermodynamics is the study of heat and how it moves and interacts with matter. One of Einstein's early contributions to the field emerged during his research into **Brownian motion** in 1905. It says that if a dust particle is diffusing randomly through the air, then the distance that the particle can travel from its starting point, as a result of random **collisions with atoms** in the air knocking it this way and that, can be determined from a simple mathematical equation—called the "**Einstein relation**." The equation involves the air temperature, the size of the particles, and the drag force acting on them as they move through the air.

Critical opalescence

In 1910 Einstein developed a theory of a phenomenon called "critical opalescence," in which some liquid mixtures can suddenly assume a milky appearance above a certain temperature. A familiar example is the way phenol-based household disinfectants turn cloudy when they are mixed with water. Einstein's theory puts the effect down to fluctuations in the concentration of the mixture that cause corresponding fluctuations in the "**refractive index**"—the degree to which it **bends light rays** passing through it. Einstein used thermodynamic considerations to show that above a critical temperature—which depends upon the composition and concentration of the mixture—these fluctuations become large, scattering white light randomly in all directions so that the liquid itself appears white.

The Einstein refrigerator

Twice in his life, Albert Einstein collaborated with the Hungarian physicist **Leó Szilárd**. The second time was when they wrote to President Roosevelt on the eve of the Second World War alerting him to the potentially devastating power of nuclear chain reactions, and warning that Germany might try to build an **atomic bomb**. The first time was when they built a refrigerator. Their design—which, perhaps unfairly to Szilárd, became known simply as the "Einstein refrigerator"—had no moving parts, operating solely on the flow of pressurized gases, and required no electricity, just a heat source. The device was granted a **US patent** in 1930, but was soon superseded by more modern compressor-based fridges, which were more efficient. In 2008, however, it was reported that scientists at Oxford University were developing the idea with a view to applying it in areas of the world without electricity.

3-second Brief

Einstein proves himself the master of heat science by figuring out why liquids go cloudy and co-inventing a refrigerator that doesn't need to be plugged in.

Related Thoughts

see also
THE WAR YEARS
page 52
STATISTICAL MECHANICS
page 94

"Classical thermodynamics... It is the only physical theory of universal content which I am convinced will never be overthrown."

Nov. 11, 1930. A. EINSTEIN ET AL 1,781,541

REFRIGERATION

Filed Dec. 16, 1927

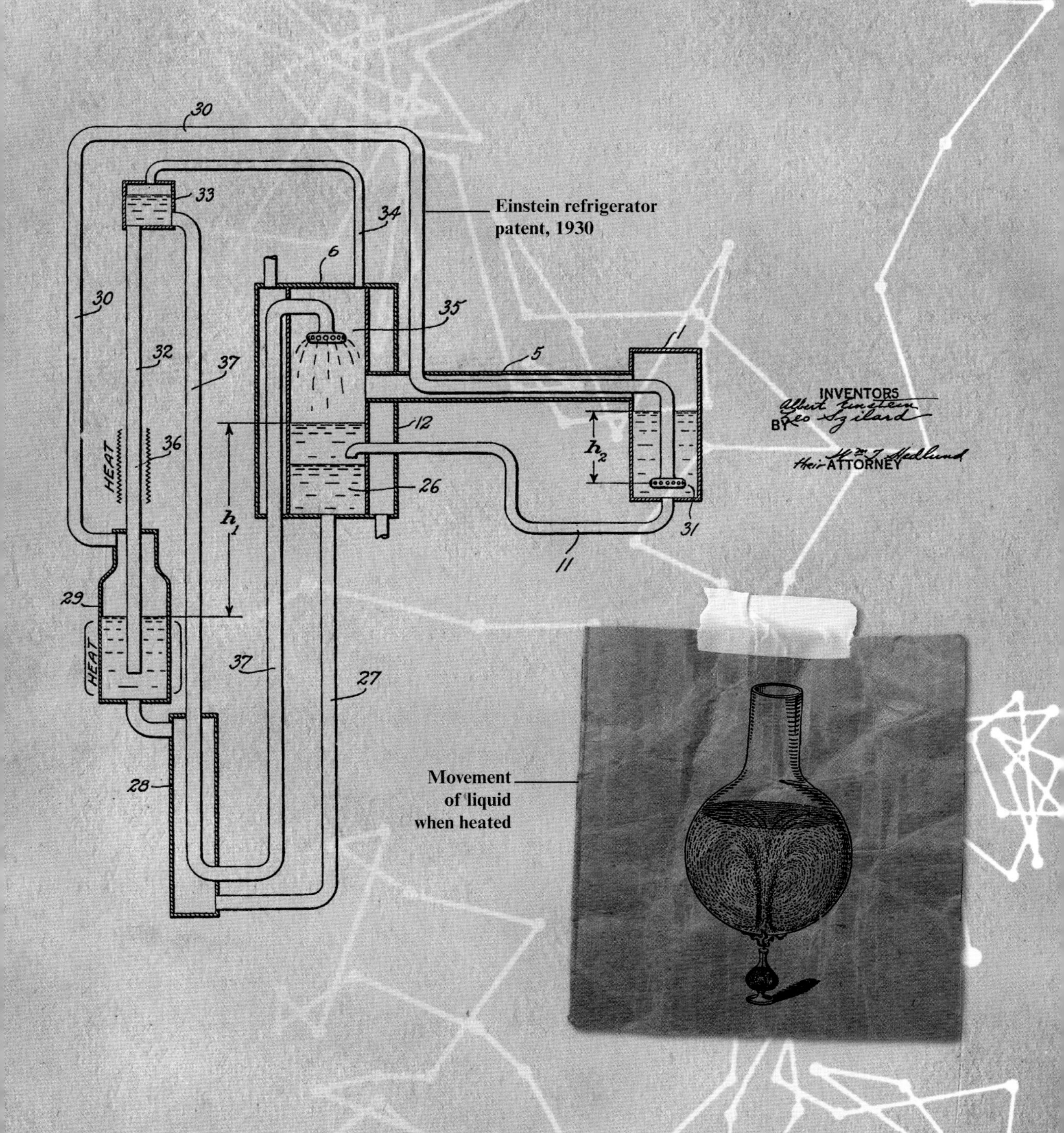

Einstein refrigerator patent, 1930

Movement of liquid when heated

Electromagnetism

Photoelectric effect

Shine a light on a metal and it'll give off electrons. This is the photoelectric effect. It was first noticed in 1887 by German physicist **Heinrich Hertz**. But below a certain cut-off frequency (corresponding to ultraviolet light) Hertz noticed that no electrons were emitted, and explaining why was taxing the best scientific brains. Einstein provided the answer in 1905 by drawing upon an idea that had been put forward five years earlier by his colleague Max Planck. He had supposed that light comes in discrete packets known as "**quanta**," with the energy of each being proportional to the **light's frequency**. Einstein realized electrons are emitted because of collisions with the light quanta, and that this can only happen if the energy of each one is sufficient to overcome the forces holding the electrons in place. In Planck's model of light that's only possible when the frequency is high enough.

3-second Brief

Einstein figures out how electrons can be generated by light and tries to fathom the nature of superconductors. Along the way he confirms suspicions that light is quantized.

Einstein-de Haas effect

In 1915, the same year as the general theory of relativity was published, Einstein worked with the Dutch physicist **Wander Johannes de Haas** to work out the connection between the magnetic field of a conductor and the **quantum spin** of the electron particles within it. They found that when a magnetic material such as iron is suspended within a **conducting coil**, then the magnetic field created by the coil causes the material to rotate. A law called the conservation of angular momentum says that rotation can neither be created nor destroyed and so the rotation of the material must be balanced by an equal, but opposite, rotation inside it. They interpreted this (correctly) as the spin of its **electrons**, all aligned in the same direction by the field.

Related Thoughts

see also
OTHER HONORS
page 42
CONSEQUENCES OF THE SPECIAL THEORY
page 78

Superconductivity

In 1911, Dutch physicist **Heike Kamerlingh Onnes** discovered that when some metals are cooled to within a whisker of absolute zero, –459.67°F (–273°C), their electrical resistance abruptly vanishes. Onnes demonstrated this phenomenon, which he called "**superconductivity**," using mercury cooled down to –452.2°F (–269°C). In 1922, Einstein published a theoretical study of the effect in which he suggested that the current is carried along linked strands of molecules called "**conduction chains**." He speculated that superconductivity is only seen at low temperature because heat disrupts these chains. Alas, this time he was wrong. The physics needed to explain the phenomenon simply hadn't been invented yet, and the correct theory of superconductivity didn't come along until 1957.

"I have now found in a most simple way the relation between the size of elementary quanta of matter and the wavelengths of radiation."

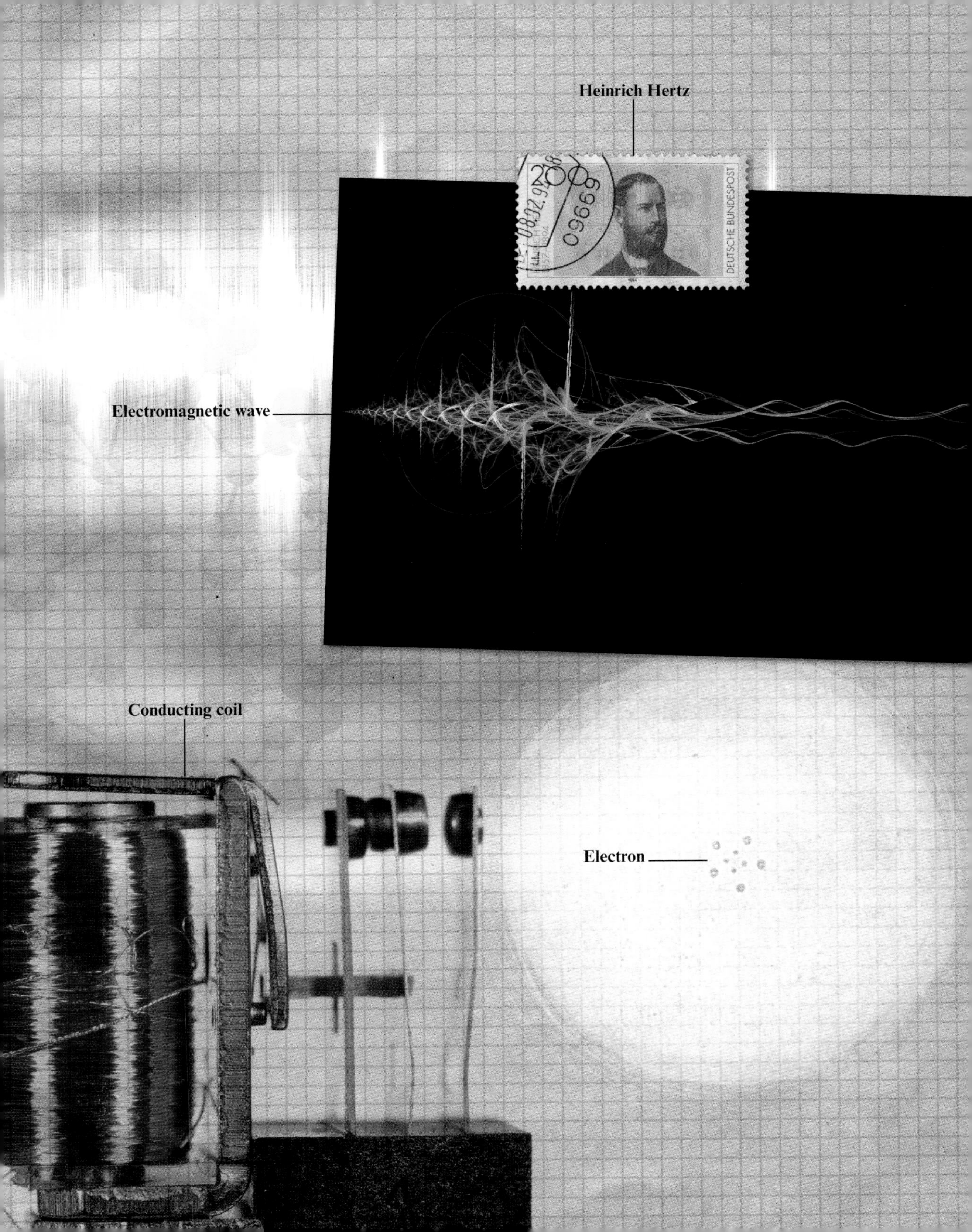

Heinrich Hertz
Electromagnetic wave
Conducting coil
Electron
DEUTSCHE BUNDESPOST

Foundations of the Special Theory

The ether

During the nineteenth century, physicists believed that light waves were ripples in a substance pervading the whole of space, known as the "ether"—rather like ripples moving across the surface of a pond. But in 1887, two American physicists—**Albert Michelson** and **Edward Morley**—carried out an experiment to try to detect the motion of the Earth relative to the ether as it **orbited around the Sun**. They found nothing. This prompted Dutch theoretical physicist **Hendrik Lorentz** to put forward a theory that could explain the null result if objects physically shrink as they move. Einstein argued that if Lorentz's theory was correct, then this shrinking should be independent of the mechanical properties of objects—and should instead be a fundamental feature of space and time.

The principle of relativity

There was another reason why Einstein didn't like the ether. If this nebulous substance that light moved through did exist, then it would define a preferred frame of reference in the Universe. Two centuries earlier **Isaac Newton** had argued in favor of just such a preferred reference frame, a concept he called "**absolute space**." But Einstein hated the idea. He believed instead that all frames of reference in the Universe were equally valid, and that any physical theory had to embrace this notion—which he called the **principle of relativity**.

The speed of light

Generally speaking, there is relative motion between two moving objects. So, for example, if two vehicles are heading toward each other at 60mph (97kph) then the driver of each will see the other approaching at a relative speed of 120mph (194kph). You might expect the same logic to apply to beams of light—if you could pull alongside a light beam, then another beam coming in the opposite direction would travel relative to you at **twice the speed**. But there was a problem with this. In 1861, Scottish physicist James Clerk Maxwell had put forward his revolutionary theory of electromagnetism. It predicted that the speed of light is a fundamental constant of nature. If light beams obeyed the usual **laws of relative motion**, then this would be at odds with the principle of relativity—how could light speed be a constant and yet vary relative to the motion of an observer? Einstein's solution was to postulate that light travels at the same speed in all frames of reference. It was this great insight that led him directly, in 1905, to **special theory of relativity**.

3-second Brief

At the turn of the century, something wasn't quite right in physics. The laws of mechanics and electromagnetism didn't add up. Einstein had a pretty good idea why.

Related Thoughts

see also
THE SPECIAL THEORY OF RELATIVITY
page 76
FOUNDATIONS OF THE GENERAL THEORY
page 80

"There is no logical way to the discovery of these elemental laws. There is only the way of intuition..."

Apex of
Earth's way
Direction of Earth's motion
& of increasing longitude
Sunrise
Earth
Sunset
Sun
Anti-apex
Albert
Michelson

The Special Theory of Relativity

Time and space

Einstein's solution to the disparities between Maxwell's theory of electromagnetism and the **laws of relative motion** became known as the "special theory of relativity." The crux of the theory was a set of equations linking the properties of objects as measured in frames of reference moving at different speeds. At slow speeds the equations boiled down to the usual common-sense laws where, for example, the speeds of two vehicles approaching one another simply add together. But at high speed Einstein's new laws were wildly different. They predicted Lorentz's contraction rule, where fast-moving objects get shorter in their direction of travel. Another effect is "**time dilation**," in which a moving clock ticks slower than one that's stationary, meaning that a rapidly moving object ages more slowly than one that's at rest. According to time dilation, an astronaut who travels at 99 percent **light speed** for a year will return to find seven years have passed back on Earth.

3-second Brief

At a stroke, Albert Einstein rewrites the book of classical mechanics—which had taken intellectual giants such as Newton and Galileo centuries to put together.

Simultaneity

Relativity means that two events measured as occurring simultaneously in one person's frame of reference are not necessarily simultaneous in the reference frame of someone who's moving differently. Imagine a light bulb in the center of a moving railway carriage. An observer in the carriage switches the light on and sees it illuminate both ends of the carriage **simultaneously**. But an observer standing on a platform as the train passes sees the beam strike the back of the carriage first. According to Einstein's theory, relative to the stationary observer the **light has the same speed** despite the motion of the train. And so they see the back of the carriage moving toward the light while the front is moving away from it, which is why it hits the back of the carriage first.

Related Thoughts

see also
ZURICH POLYTECHNIC
page 28
FOUNDATIONS OF THE SPECIAL THEORY
page 74

The fourth dimension

The special theory of relativity shook up physics in a big way, but most **radical** of all was its treatment of time. Before Einstein's theory, physicists considered the **three dimensions of space** and one of time to be very different entities. Relativity brought them together, with time emerging as the fourth dimension of a **unified fabric** that physicists called "**spacetime**." Ironically, much of the work on the spacetime physics of relativity was done by German mathematician Hermann Minkowski. He had been Einstein's math tutor at Zurich Polytechnic, where he famously referred to the less-than-motivated young Einstein as a "lazy dog."

"The faster you go, the shorter you are."

Einstein's
Special Theory of Relativity

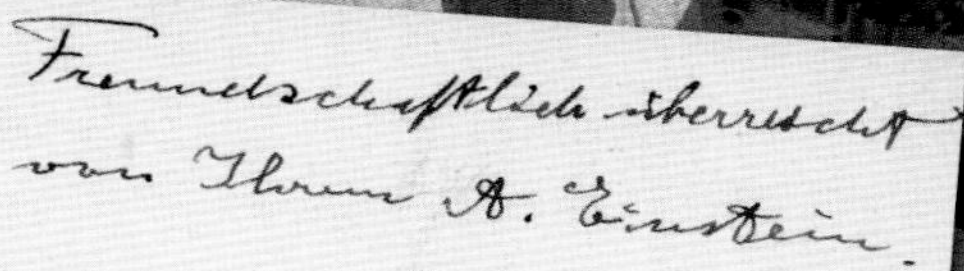
Freundschaftlich überreicht
von Ihrem A. Einstein.

Über die spezielle und die allgemeine Relativitätstheorie

(Gemeinverständlich)

Von

A. EINSTEIN

Mit 3 Figuren

Dieses Exemplar ist
das erste, welches die
Druckerpresse verlassen hat.
Es wurde mir von
Herrn Prof. Einstein zugeschickt, unmittelbar nachdem
er es empfangen hatte,
kurz bevor ich nach
Frankreich ins Feld ging.
Hans Mühsam.
Berlin / z. Z. Französische
Front. April 1917.

SAMMLUNG VIEWEG

Braunschweig
Druck und Verlag von Friedr. Vieweg & Sohn
1917

Consequences of the Special Theory

Cosmic speed limit

The special theory of relativity rules out the possibility of motion at faster than the speed of light. The theory says that if such "**superluminal**" travel is allowed, then it's possible for the order of cause and effect to become reversed, leading to **paradoxical situations** in which outcomes can happen before the events that caused them. This universal speed restriction manifests itself by making it increasingly harder for objects to accelerate as they approach the speed of light. The faster you go, the more energy it takes to accelerate further until—at the speed of light—the energy needed becomes **infinite**.

$E=mc^2$

Probably the most famous equation in the whole of physics, $E=mc^2$ drops directly out of the mathematics of the special theory. It's a relationship between **energy** (E), **mass** (m), and the **speed of light** (c), and essentially says that mass and energy are equivalent. If you measure the initial mass of a lump of **coal** and then measure the mass of all the ash and smoke after it's been burned, you will find that the mass after is less than the mass before—with the difference in mass multiplied by c^2 giving you the total energy released during burning. Einstein considered $E=mc^2$ to be so important that he dedicated an entire scientific paper to it. And he was right—it would later become a keystone in the **theory of nuclear energy**.

Quantum spin

Subatomic particles exhibit a property that physicists call "quantum spin." It's quite different from the spin that we're used to in the everyday world, which is a property of motion, like speed and acceleration. Instead, Quantum spin is a fundamental property of particles, more like mass and electric charge. In 1924, Austrian physicist **Wolfgang Pauli** proposed a mathematical description of quantum spin. While it seemed to work, even he had no idea exactly what the physical basis for his theory was. That was provided three years later by the British theoretical physicist Paul Dirac. He was able to derive Pauli's equations of quantum spin by applying the special theory of relativity to the laws of **quantum theory**, the physics governing the behavior of the subatomic world. Einstein's theory was starting to make its presence felt in the most unexpected of areas.

3-second Brief

The special theory of relativity, initially developed to explain the relative motion between two moving bodies, changes the entire face of theoretical physics.

Related Thoughts

see also

ENERGY
page 114

FASTER THAN LIGHT
page 128

"It followed from the special theory of relativity that mass and energy are both but different manifestations of the same thing."

Light
e = mc²
Energy
Mass

Foundations of the General Theory

Acceleration

Einstein knew that the special theory was incomplete, because it applied only to the special case of objects traveling at uniform speed—that's why it's called "special." Between 1905 and 1915 he set about **generalizing** the theory to include the motion of objects that are accelerating. This would mean building into his theory the concept of "**inertia**"—the way heavy objects (like an automobile) take more effort to accelerate than lighter objects (like, say, a shopping cart). Einstein believed that the correct treatment of inertia would emerge by making his theory consistent with what he called "**Mach's principle**." This was an idea that had been propounded by Austrian physicist Ernst Mach, which in essence said that inertia arises from the motion of objects relative to the rest of the mass in the Universe.

Gravity

Einstein was also aware that the special theory was inconsistent with gravity. The best theory of gravity at the time was Isaac Newton's law of **universal gravitation**, which had held sway since 1687. This said that gravity propagates through space infinitely fast—if the Sun suddenly disappeared, then the Earth and all the other planets would instantaneously stop feeling the gravitational force holding them in their orbits and would fly off into space. But this was clearly at odds with the special theory of relativity, within which nothing—gravity included—can move faster than the **speed of light**. In fact, sunlight takes **8.3 minutes** to reach the Earth and so any change in the Sun's gravity can't make itself felt any quicker than that. Einstein thus realized that the generalized version of relativity would probably involve a rewrite of Newton's laws of gravity.

The equivalence principle

Early on in the **development** of the general theory of relativity it dawned on Einstein that both of these concepts were intimately entwined—gravity and acceleration were **equivalent**. A person in a sealed box experiencing an acceleration pushing them toward the floor would be unable to tell whether that acceleration is caused by the box being suspended in a gravitational field (like the acceleration that's pressing you into your seat as you read this), or caused because the box itself is gathering speed (like the acceleration you feel pushing you backward in an aircraft as it speeds up). Einstein called this the "**equivalence principle**."

3-second Brief

Realizing that the special theory of relativity is incomplete as it stands, Einstein embarks on the most arduous, and yet most rewarding, intellectual journey of his life.

Related Thoughts

see also
THE SPECIAL THEORY OF RELATIVITY
page 76
THE GENERAL THEORY OF RELATIVITY
page 82

"The happiest thought in my life..."
ON REALIZING GRAVITY AND ACCELERATION ARE EQUIVALENT

Sir Isaac Newton

The General Theory of Relativity

Spacetime curvature

By 1912, it had already occurred to Einstein that one route to his new theory could be to bend the flat "**spacetime**" of the special theory. After all, gravity causes the paths of objects moving through space to curve. Einstein became convinced of the fact when he considered the behavior of a simple rotating disk. Rotation is a form of acceleration (the acceleration inside a rotating spin dryer is what makes your clothes stick to the drum). Because of the **Lorentz contraction effect** the outer circumference of the disk must get shorter the faster it spins. However, the radius of the disk remains the same. The only way this is possible is if the disk becomes deformed into a kind of dish shape. Space and time, it seemed, really were **curved**.

3-second Brief

Einstein calls upon the esoteric mathematics of curved spaces to turn the special theory of relativity into a new model of gravity, in which mass and energy deform space and time.

The Einstein tensor

But how was Einstein going to build these geometric factors into his mathematical theory? With the help of his friend and colleague **Marcel Grossman**, who was an expert on geometry, he turned to a branch of math developed during the latter half of the nineteenth century by the German mathematician Bernhard Riemann. Called "**differential geometry**," it's a way of using equations to represent how points on an arbitrarily curved surface are connected to one another. This is done using a mathematical entity called a "**tensor**," a two-dimensional array of numbers—a bit like a matrix—that gives the distance between any two points in the space. After much trial and error, Einstein found a tensor that described the gravitational curvature of space. It's now known as the "Einstein tensor."

Related Thoughts

see also

FOUNDATIONS OF THE SPECIAL THEORY
page 74
THE SPECIAL THEORY OF RELATIVITY
page 76

The field equation

All that remained to do now was to link the Einstein tensor to the contents of space and time—the matter responsible for generating the gravitational field in the first place. For the general theory of relativity this turned out to be another tensor. Its components take account of not just the amount of mass present but also the **energy**—for example, as radiation (as might be expected from $E=mc^2$)—as well as the **momentum**, pressure, and stresses present within the matter. The Einstein field equation, which is the **linchpin** of the general theory of relativity, amounts to a simple formula linking this "energy-momentum tensor" to the Einstein tensor.

"The theory is of incomparable beauty."

Curvature of
space and time

The Race to Relativity

David Hilbert

In June 1915, Einstein visited the **University of Göttingen** in Germany to deliver a series of lectures about his embryonic general theory of relativity. In the audience was a brilliant mathematician by the name of David Hilbert. Einstein was struggling to deduce the final form of his field equation, and Hilbert was so intrigued by the problem he began to study it carefully himself. He soon spotted an **error in Einstein's draft theory** (the "Entwurf," as it was known) and set about correcting it. When Einstein learned of Hilbert's breakthrough he redoubled his efforts, working around the clock to bring the theory to completion. In the end, both men arrived at the correct equations at around the same time—late **November 1915**. Many even believe Hilbert actually got there first, although Hilbert made no claim to be the originator of the general theory of relativity and gave Einstein full credit. Einstein was burned-out by the whole experience, stating in a letter to his friend Michele Besso that he was "**contented but kaput**."

3-second Brief

Einstein is almost beaten to the discovery of the general theory of relativity field equation and works himself to the brink of exhaustion in order to get there first.

The Einstein-Hilbert action

Hilbert used a very different mathematical method to Einstein. Einstein was trying plausible incarnations of the **field equations** and then checking to see whether they gave the same results in all coordinate systems, so as to preserve his cherished principle of relativity. Hilbert, on the other hand, decided to take a more **systematic approach**, trying to derive the equations directly from what's called an "action." This is a measure of the energy locked away in a system. You can work out the equations of motion for any system by demanding that its action is always minimized—equivalent to saying that nature takes the **path of least resistance**. And this is what Hilbert did. The action for the general theory of relativity is now known as the Einstein-Hilbert action.

Related Thoughts

see also

BERN
page 32

THE GENERAL THEORY OF RELATIVITY
page 82

Henri Poincaré

To Einstein, the whole affair must have seemed like **déjà vu**. Ten years earlier, while developing the special theory of relativity, he had almost been beaten to the pinch by the French mathematician **Henri Poincaré**. Indeed, mathematically speaking he was. Poincaré had already arrived at the same mathematics as Einstein. But he failed to recognize the revolutionary new picture of space and time that his equations were showing to him. It took Einstein's great **intuition** as a physicist to make this step, and that's why Einstein is rightly credited as the originator of the theory.

"The system you furnish agrees—as far as I can see—exactly with what I found in the last few weeks and have presented to the Academy."

LETTER TO DAVID HILBERT

welche Allgemeinheit als gültig vermutet wurde, entwic

19. Jahrhundert wesentlich als eine Folge eines Satzes der

welche ein Pendel, dessen Masse zwischen

A und B hin und her schwingt.

B) verschwindet die Geschwindigkeit

Masse (m) steht um h höher als

im Punkte C der Bahn. In C

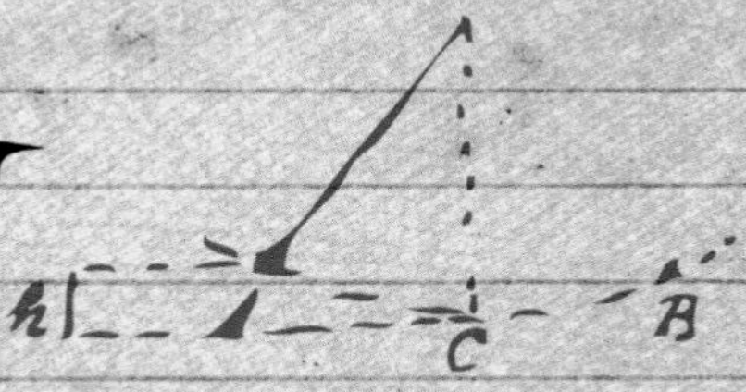

ist eine verloren gegangen; dafür aber hat die Masse eine Geschwindig-

keit v. Es ist, wie wenn sich Hubhöhe in Geschwindig-

keit restlos verwandeln könnten. Die exakte Bezie-

h A C B

$$mgh = \frac{m}{2} v^2,$$

gesamte Lage ... der Erdschwere bedeutet. Das Inter-

dass diese Beziehung unabhängig ist von der Länge

auszeichnet von der Form der Bahn, in welcher die M

Interpretation: Es gibt etwas (nämlich die Energie) ... Energie

des Vorgangs erhalten bleibt. In A ist die Energie der Be-

wegung oder „potentielle Energie“, in C eine Energie der Bewegung ... das Wesen der Sache

„Energie“. Wenn diese Auffassung

richtig erfasst, so muss die Summe

$mgh + m\frac{v^2}{2}$

denselben Wert haben, ... bestätigen

alle Zwischenlagen

Consequences of the General Theory

The new Solar System

The general theory of relativity brought a wholesale shift in the way physicists thought about gravity. Rather than envisaging a **force** exchanged directly by massive bodies, gravity was now a mechanism for shaping the landscape of spacetime upon which these objects move. The Sun no longer tugs directly on the planets of the **Solar System** to hold them in their respective orbits. The planets simply travel through space while the Sun's mass deforms that space—turning it from being a straight road into a **looped circuit**. It's almost like the space of the Solar System is a giant rubber sheet, with the Sun sitting at the middle like a huge bowling ball. This creates a big depression in the sheet, around which planets then roll like marbles.

Gravitational redshift

There were some more **subtle consequences** of the general theory of relativity, too. In Einstein's theory gravity acts upon light as well as on matter, and that causes a light beam to lose energy as it climbs out of a gravitational field. Because the energy of a beam of light is directly proportional to its frequency, a **high-frequency** beam (such as blue light) gets shifted to lower frequency (i.e. toward the red) as it climbs. This is why the effect is known as the "gravitational redshift." A related phenomenon also makes clocks run slower in a gravitational field. Just as rapid motion causes time dilation in the special theory so the acceleration exerted on an object by gravity creates its own "**gravitational time dilation**" effect.

Frame dragging

Spacetime and matter can couple together in some odd ways. One is a phenomenon called "**frame dragging**," whereby spinning objects seem to drag space and time around with them—rather like the way a spoon twisting round in a tin of treacle drags the treacle round with it. The effect was originally derived from Einstein's theory by two Austrian physicists, **Josef Lense** and **Hans Thirring**, in 1918. In 1921, Einstein himself built upon their analysis to show that frame dragging also implies that the inertia of a body (its resistance to motion) increases according to how much matter there is nearby. He considered this deduction to be of great importance as it seemed to be corroborative evidence that his theory incorporated **Mach's principle**, which he had hoped from the outset it would.

3-second Brief

The general theory of relativity has dramatic ramifications for theoretical physics. Newton's applecart is completely overturned. Einstein is pleased.

Related Thoughts

see also

THE SPECIAL THEORY OF RELATIVITY
page 76

FOUNDATIONS OF THE GENERAL THEORY
page 80

"If we knew what it was we were doing, it would not be called research, would it?"

The Solar System
The whirlpool galaxy

The Evidence for Relativity

Decaying particles

The special theory of relativity is confirmed on an almost daily basis in **particle accelerators**. These are machines that whirl subatomic particles up to near lightspeed and then collide them, cracking them apart to reveal their internal workings. Some of the fragments that fly out from these **collisions** decay naturally into other particles—doing so over very precisely determined timescales. But when the fragments are moving extremely fast—as they are in a particle accelerator—these timescales are radically distorted by time dilation. Measurements of **decay times** made at particle accelerators the world over are invariably found to be in exact agreement with relativity's time-stretching predictions.

Mercury's orbit

It had long been known to astronomers that the orbit of the planet Mercury wasn't behaving itself. All the other planets go round the Sun following well-defined **elliptical orbits**. Mercury, however, is traveling around an ellipse that itself seems to rotate around the Sun—tracing out a rosette-like pattern. This problem was known as the "**perihelion precession**." Some astronomers suggested there was another undiscovered planet lurking inside Mercury's orbit, which they called "**Vulcan**," and that the influence of its gravitational tugs were throwing Mercury off course. However, when Mercury's orbit was re-analyzed within the context of the general theory of relativity it soon became clear that there was no need for Vulcan—the perihelion precession was fully explained by Einstein's general theory.

Bending of light

The benchmark test of the general theory is the **bending of starlight** by the gravity of the Sun. This was first measured in 1919 by the British astronomer **Sir Arthur Eddington**. The degree of bending was predicted to be tiny—about 1.7 seconds of arc, where 1 arcsecond is 1/3600th of a degree. A star, the position of which is being deflected by such a small amount, would still be lost in the Sun's glare. So astronomers waited for a **total eclipse**, when the bright disk of the Sun is blotted out by the silhouette of the Moon. In 1919 just such an opportunity arose and Eddington led an expedition to observe it from the island of Príncipe, off West Africa, which lay on the eclipse shadow's path. The weather wasn't good, but through breaks in the clouds Eddington obtained the pictures he needed. When he analyzed them he found his results to be exactly in line with relativity's predictions.

3-second Brief

It's sometimes said that extraordinary claims demand extraordinary evidence. That's certainly true for relativity. Though even before the evidence turned up, Einstein knew his theory was right.

Related Thoughts

see also
THE SPECIAL THEORY OF RELATIVITY
page 76
ASTROPHYSICS
page 136

"If the facts don't fit the theory, change the facts."

Particle collision
Sir Arthur
Eddington

Extending the General Theory

Gravitational lensing

Eddington's measurement of starlight bending around the Sun in 1919 was an impressive demonstration of how gravity deforms space. In 1936, Einstein scaled this up massively. He published a research paper detailing how light crossing the Universe from **distant celestial bodies** could be bent by the gravity of intervening objects. He speculated that the effect could be useful to astronomers, with the bending of light around the intervening object mimicking the action of a lens in a telescope to actually magnify the image of the distant body. The first example of this "**gravitational lensing**" effect was discovered in 1979 when astronomers realized that the Double Quasar in the constellation of Ursa Major was actually two lensed images of the same object.

3-second Brief

Einstein and other theorists take the general theory of relativity to the next level, showing how it leads to ripples in space and enables astronomers to use gravity as a sort of giant telescope.

Gravitational waves

Maxwell's theory of electromagnetism predicts **electromagnetic waves**—of which light and radio waves are examples. In much the same way, Einstein showed that the general theory of relativity allows for so-called gravitational waves, ripples in the curvature of spacetime that make their presence felt by exerting a brief wobble of gravitational force as they pass. Gravitational waves are only given off by **accelerating gravitational sources**, and even then they are feeble—unless the gravity of the source is exceptionally strong. No one has yet detected a gravitational wave, despite several elaborate observatories being built around the world to do so. However, observations of a **double neutron star system** in the constellation of Aquila have shown the two stars to be gradually coalescing at exactly the rate expected if gravitational waves were carrying away energy from the system.

Related Thoughts

see also

UNIFIED FIELD THEORY
page 100

ASTROPHYSICS
page 136

Einstein-Cartan theory

In 1922, the French physicist **Élie Cartan** proposed a modification to the general theory of relativity to include torsion—that is, **rotational forces**—in the energy-momentum tensor describing the source of the gravitational field. Cartan's mathematical formalism was completely consistent with the idea of quantum spin. Einstein was so impressed, he took a similar approach with his 1928 **theory of teleparallelism**—one of many attempts he made to construct a unified field theory. Neither teleparallelism nor Einstein-Cartan theory amounted to much in the 1920s. More recently, however, Einstein-Cartan theory has been resurrected by researchers trying to marry the general theory of relativity to quantum theory. They believe the way it handles **spin** makes it particularly amenable to quantization.

"Life is like riding a bicycle. To keep your balance you must keep moving."

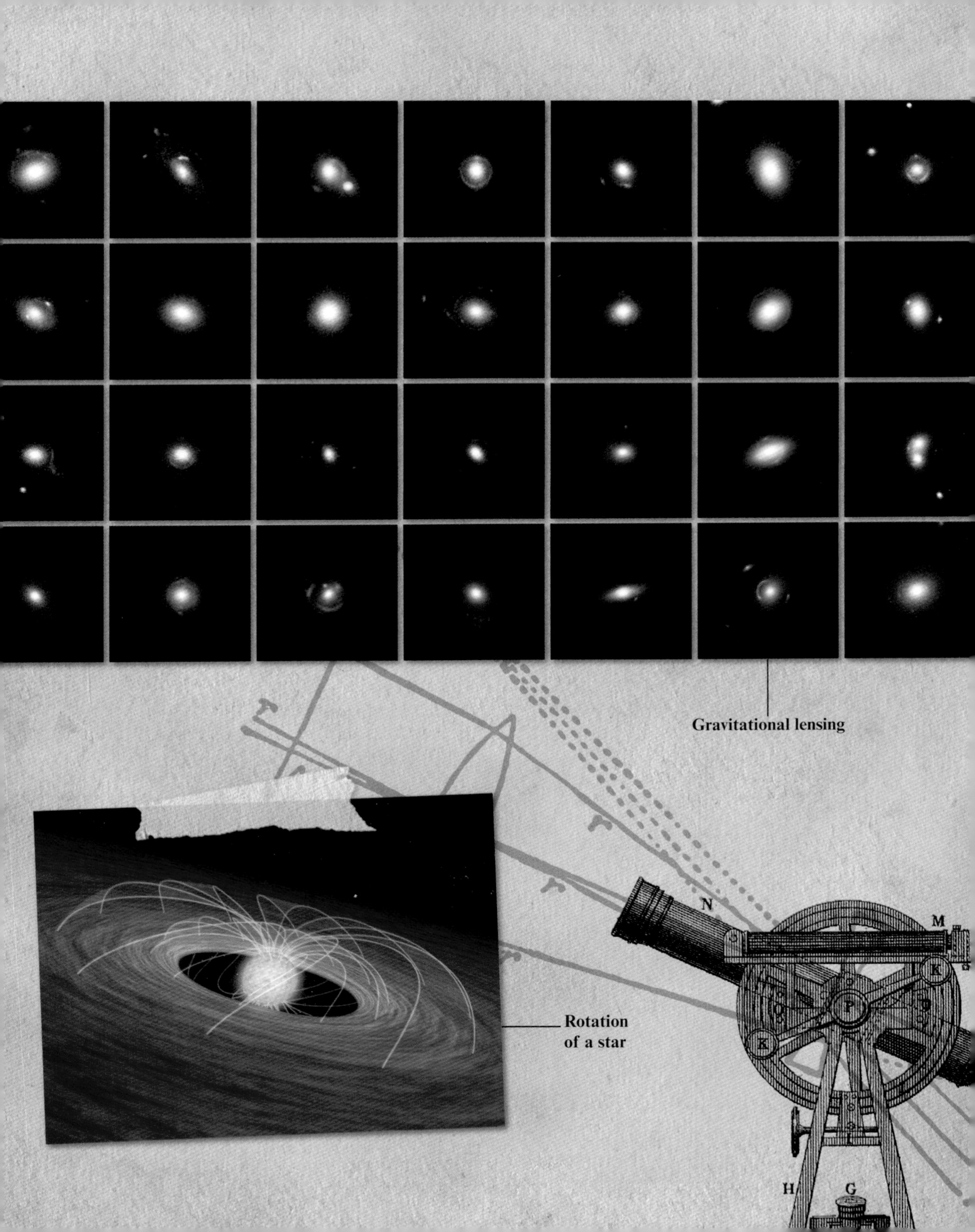

Gravitational lensing
Rotation
of a star
N
M
K
P
K
H
G

Black Holes

Dark stars

One of the most incredible concepts that general theory was able to elegantly explain is the idea that there can be regions of space where the gravity is so strong that not even light can escape. Most of Einstein's early calculations with the general theory involved approximation techniques—so formidable were the mathematics describing the theory. But in 1917, German physicist **Karl Schwarzschild** produced the first exact solution. It described the gravitational field surrounding a **static lump of matter**. Schwarzschild's solution predicted that if matter is compressed down within a certain size, which has since become known as the "Schwarzschild radius," then it becomes so dense that its gravity can prevent light beams from escaping. Such objects have since been named "**black holes**."

Horizons and singularities

Numerically, the **Schwarzschild radius** is given by the formula $2Gm/c^2$, where "c" is the speed of light, "G" is Newton's gravitational constant, and "m" is the mass. The Schwarzschild radius of the Sun is just 1.86 miles (3km). If you could squash the Sun down this small (and there are mechanisms in physics by which the cores of stars can be compressed, such as supernova explosions) then the result is a black hole. The hole's outer boundary (equal in size to the Schwarzschild radius) is known as the "**event horizon**." Because not even light can escape from within the event horizon—and nothing can travel faster than light—then anything falling over the horizon can never return. Instead it's doomed to fall to the hole's center where it's crushed at a point of infinite density known as a "singularity."

Wormholes

Einstein disliked the idea that physical quantities could become infinite, as they would have to in the singularity at the heart of a black hole. In 1935, he and his Princeton colleague **Nathan Rosen** discovered a way out of this apparent impasse. Schwarzschild's equations were equally valid if the distance, "r," from a black hole's center was replaced by "–r." Einstein and Rosen wondered if it might be possible to pass through the singularity and emerge into a new region of space, albeit one with negative coordinates. When they investigated further they found that it was. Their solution became known as the "**Einstein-Rosen bridge**"—but it is better known today as a "**wormhole**."

3-second Brief

It soon becomes clear that relativity admits the bizarre possibility of holes in space. Ever the opportunist, Einstein figures out how to travel through them.

Related Thoughts

see also
FASTER THAN LIGHT
page 128
ASTROPHYSICS
page 136

"Imagination is more important than knowledge. Knowledge is limited."

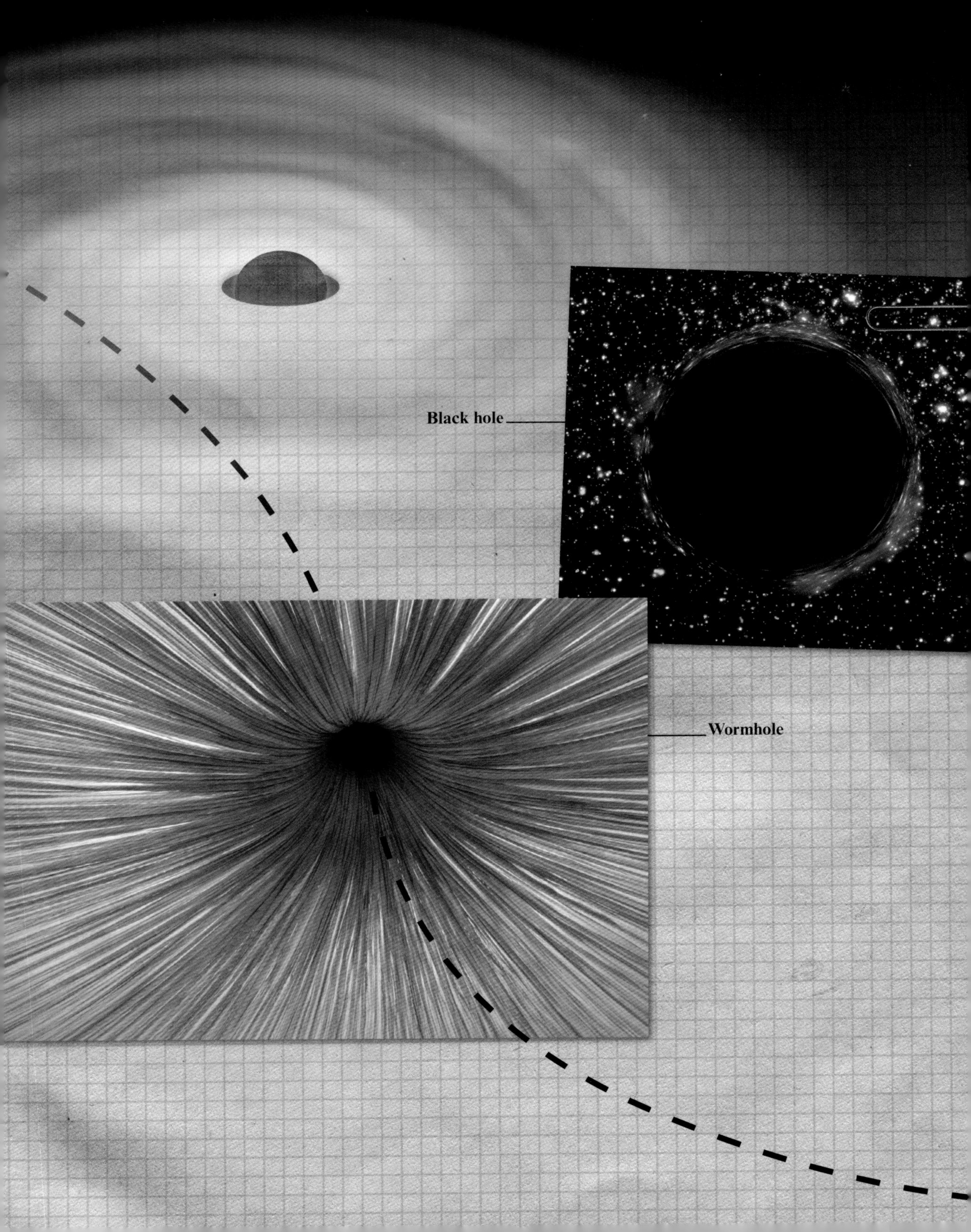
Black hole
Wormhole

Statistical Mechanics

Brownian motion

Brownian motion is **random movement** exhibited by particles suspended in a fluid—either a gas or liquid. It's named after the nineteenth-century Scottish botanist **Robert Brown**, who noticed this jittery motion in microscopic dust particles found in the cavities inside pollen grains. In 1905, Einstein constructed a theory that explained Brownian motion as being caused by random collisions of the particles with atoms in the air. Even though an individual atom is too small to influence a dust particle on its own, random variations in the number of atoms striking the particle from every direction can indeed make it lurch this way and that. A convincing mathematical explanation for Brownian motion had evaded physicists for a century. Einstein's model also provided the first hard evidence that **atoms really exist**.

Bose-Einstein statistics

In deriving his Brownian motion paper, Einstein had made use of "**kinetic theory**," which says that macroscopic properties of gases and liquids—such as temperature and pressure—are caused by the motion of their **atoms and molecules**. Kinetic theory was the forerunner of the powerful "statistical mechanics" that applies complex statistical methods to particles in order to deduce the average or "bulk" properties of matter. In 1924, the Indian physicist **Satyendra Nath Bose** published one of the first theories of statistical mechanics to be consistent with the new laws of quantum theory. Bose's analysis applied only to photons: particles of light. Einstein saw the paper and realized immediately that it could be extended to gas molecules that have similar quantum spin to the photon. The theory became known as "Bose-Einstein statistics" and it accurately describes matter made from particles that have whole number or "integer" values for their spin—i.e. 0, 1, 2, 3 and so on.

Bose-Einstein condensates

Particles that obey Bose-Einstein statistics are known as **bosons**. Examples include atoms that have an even number of particles, such as **helium**. One consequence of the theory is that a gas of boson particles cooled sufficiently can suddenly drop down into the lowest energy state allowed by quantum theory—the so-called ground state. When this happens, all the particles move in unison so the gas behaves like one big particle, obeying quantum rules. This is known as a **Bose-Einstein condensate**. The first one to be created experimentally was made by researchers at the University of Colorado in 1995.

3-second Brief

Mighty oaks from little acorns grow. Einstein temporarily shelves his aversion to the quantum world and applies some small-scale laws to better understand large-scale physics.

Related Thoughts

see also
THERMODYNAMICS
page 70
CONSEQUENCES OF THE SPECIAL THEORY
page 78
PARTICLE ACCELERATORS
page 120

"Bodies on the order of magnitude 1/1000mm, suspended in liquids, must already perform an observable random motion... actually observed by physiologists who call it Brownian motion."

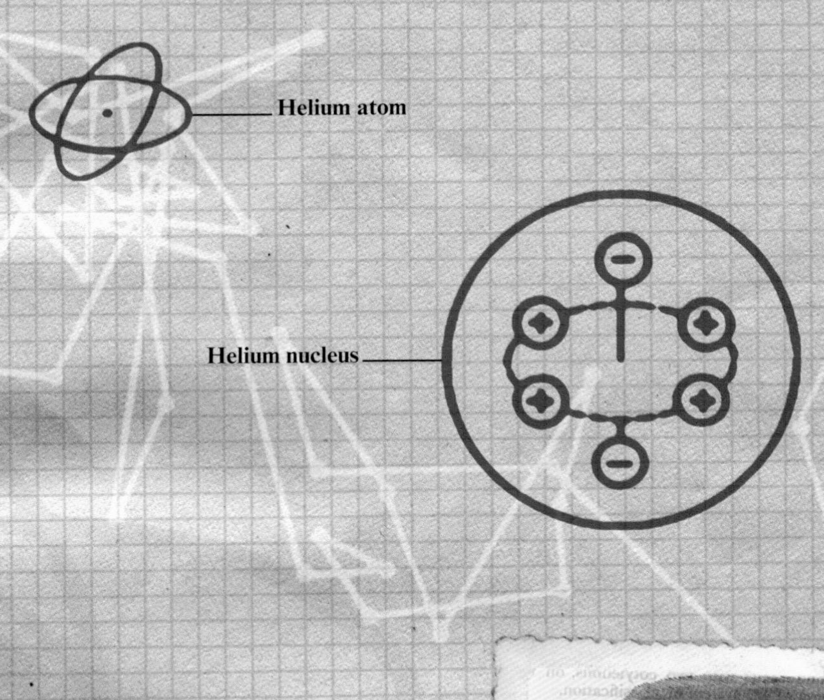
Helium atom
Helium nucleus

Robert Brown
Neon atom

The Quantum World

God does not play dice

Quantum theory is the branch of physics governing the **behavior of tiny atoms** and molecules. Einstein loathed it. This may seem odd, as his own theory of the photoelectric effect advanced the revolutionary notion that light is made of quantum particles called **photons**. But as quantum theory developed, a strand began to emerge that stuck in his craw. It was the idea of uncertainty. According to quantum theory, you can never know the exact details of a particle at any given moment in time—only the **probability** of finding it in one state or another. Einstein's hatred for this lack of determinism went with him to the grave.

3-second Brief

Despite being one of the original architects of quantum theory, Albert Einstein had a love-hate relationship with the vagaries of the subatomic world. Mostly hate.

The EPR paradox

In 1935 Einstein, together with **Nathan Rosen** and **Boris Podolsky**, published a key thought experiment. According to a common view of quantum theory—called the **Copenhagen interpretation**—particles are in an undetermined state until they are measured. Certain subatomic particles decay, breaking apart to form pairs of new particles. The particles in the pair are each guaranteed to have opposite values of a property known as spin—which can take one of two values, "up" or "down." The spin of each particle isn't known until a measurement is made, but the particles remain linked so that measuring the spin of one instantly fixes the spin of the other. Einstein pointed out that this "spooky action at a distance" means it's possible to know the state of one particle without actually measuring it, contradicting the Copenhagen view. Their thought experiment became known as the Einstein-Podolsky-Rosen (EPR) paradox and later gave birth to "**quantum entanglement**."

Related Thoughts

see also
STRUCTURE OF MATTER
page 66
NATURE OF LIGHT
page 68
QUANTUM ENTANGLEMENT
page 122

Einstein's cat

The same year, Austrian theoretical physicist **Erwin Schrödinger** came up with another quantum thought experiment. A cat is trapped in a box with a phial of poison hooked up to a hammer and a **radioactive substance**. If the source decays then the hammer falls, releasing the poison, and the cat dies. Otherwise it lives. The Copenhagen interpretation says before a measurement is made uncertainty means the substance is both decayed and not decayed—and so, before the box is opened, the cat is simultaneously dead and alive. The thought experiment is called "Schrödinger's cat." What's not so well known is that it was actually inspired by a **letter from Einstein**, in which he imagined a pile of gunpowder detonated by quantum uncertainty being simultaneously exploded and not exploded.

"The more successes the quantum theory enjoys, the sillier it looks."

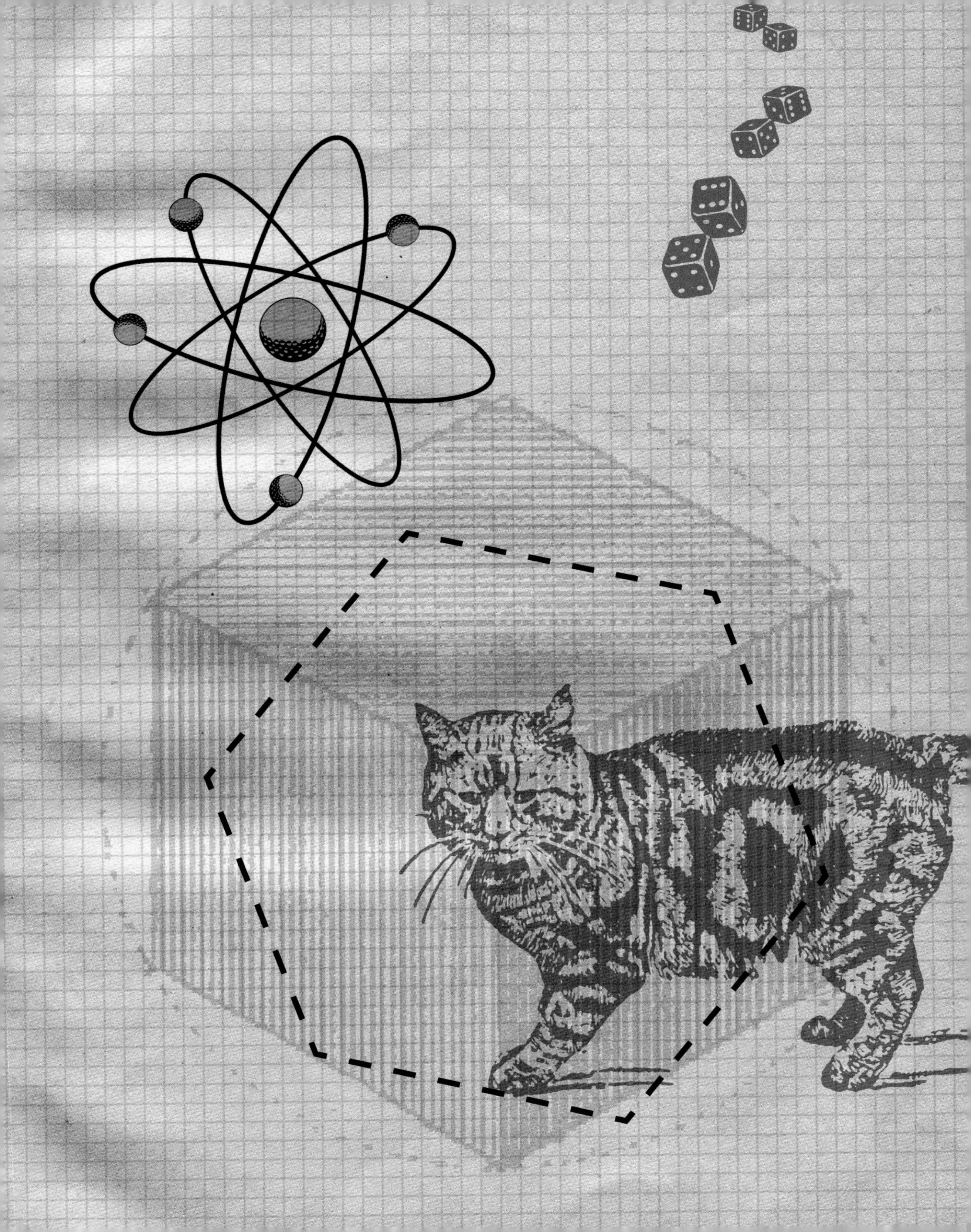

Cosmology

Spherical Universe

Many a high school physics student has probably wondered, "Where does space end?", and in 1917, Einstein used relativity to offer an answer—or, rather, to circumvent the question. Because if Einstein was right then space doesn't actually end anywhere; it has no edge. Just as asking about the edge of the Earth becomes meaningless once you realize that the planet is curved into a sphere, so Einstein proposed that the general theory might curve the space of the entire Universe into one giant **cosmic sphere** with no boundaries. Of course, the Universe isn't a two-dimensional sphere like our planet. Instead, it's spherical in **three dimensions**. Gaze far enough out into the void—in any direction—using a super-powerful **telescope** and you might just find yourself staring at the back of your own head.

What's outside?

That's all very well, but if the Universe is curved into a sphere, then what's outside the sphere? After all, we know there's a whole Universe of space lying beyond the curved surface of the Earth. So what's **beyond the Universe**? The answer, according to the general theory, is nothing. Not just empty space, but **absolutely nothing**—no space, no time, no matter, no energy. Nothing. That's because in relativity our three dimensions of space plus one of time is all there is. Unlike the surface of the Earth, which is known to be one of many planets **occupying space**, our Universe is the only one (at least, as far as we know) and there is nothing outside of it.

Creation from nothing

So the story goes, Albert Einstein was crossing the road when the revelation came. He and a colleague—the eminent Russian physicist **George Gamow**—were out for walk in Princeton one day. Gamow was explaining how one of his students had calculated that if the mass of a star could be concentrated at a point, then the **net energy** of the star is zero—because the star's mass energy is exactly equal and opposite to the energy locked away in its gravitational field. Einstein reportedly stopped dead in his tracks, causing a number of cars to swerve round him. The great man had realized that the very same principle could be applied to the Universe at large. The energy of all its planets, stars, and galaxies exactly balances its gravitational energy—so that our cosmos really could have **popped into existence** where before there was nothing at all.

3-second Brief

Einstein goes large, quite literally—applying his general theory of relativity to the entire Universe. His calculations suggest space is round, isolated, and sprang from nothing.

Related Thoughts

see also
BLACK HOLES
page 92
MODERN COSMOLOGY
page 138

"Only two things are infinite, the Universe and human stupidity—and I'm not sure about the former."

C
H
G
B
F
F
G
E
U
S
T
Q
a
a
a

Unified Field Theory

One force to rule them all

After the great triumph of relativity, Einstein spent much of his remaining years **consumed** by the search for a consolidated description of physics—the so-called **unified field theory**. At the time there were only two known forces of nature: gravity and electromagnetism. Today, there are four, with two extra forces—the weak and strong nuclear interactions—having been established in the 1950s. Einstein's goal was to merge gravity and electromagnetism into one. During the 1920s and '30s, newspaper headlines around the world proclaimed each of his new unification models as unveiling a new understanding of the **cosmos**—before a fatal flaw would inevitably arise, proving it untenable.

3-second Brief

Much of Einstein's later life is spent on a wild goose chase for a unified description of the forces of nature. Even today, physicists are uncertain such a theory exists.

Kaluza-Klein theory

One of the earliest attempts at a unified theory—and the model that inspired Einstein in his own quest—is known as the **Kaluza-Klein theory**. The foundations were laid in 1919 by German mathematician Theodor Kaluza and it was developed further by the Swedish physicist Oskar Klein. The crux of the theory is that spacetime is actually **five-dimensional**. Gravity was built into the four ordinary dimensions, while the interactions taking place in the fifth account for electromagnetism. Klein's major contribution was to explain why we don't see the fifth dimension. He argued that it's tightly curled up and so hidden from view. The size of this fifth dimension was controlled by an extra particle predicted by the theory, called the "**radion**." Although shortcomings later emerged in the Kaluza-Klein theory, it has remained a lingering paradigm in theoretical physics today with its use of extra dimensions and particles persisting in modern unification schemes, such as **string theory**.

Related Thoughts

see also

MODERN UNIFICATION THEORIES
page 118

PARTICLE ACCELERATORS
page 120

Is physics really unified?

Some scientists are skeptical that a working unified field theory—often known in modern parlance as a "**Theory of Everything**"—will ever be found. Progress has been made toward unifying some of the forces. In the 1970s, the electroweak theory successfully brought together the weak nuclear force and electromagnetism. And there have been encouraging developments with folding the strong force into the mix too. But **gravity**, Einstein's baby, still refuses to join the party. And so Einstein—probably the greatest physicist of all time—may well have spent a good deal of his life on what was ultimately a fruitless endeavor. Many consider that fact to be a **tragedy** of, well, cosmic proportions.

"There could be no fairer destiny for any physical theory than that it should point the way to a more comprehensive theory in which it lives on as a limiting case."

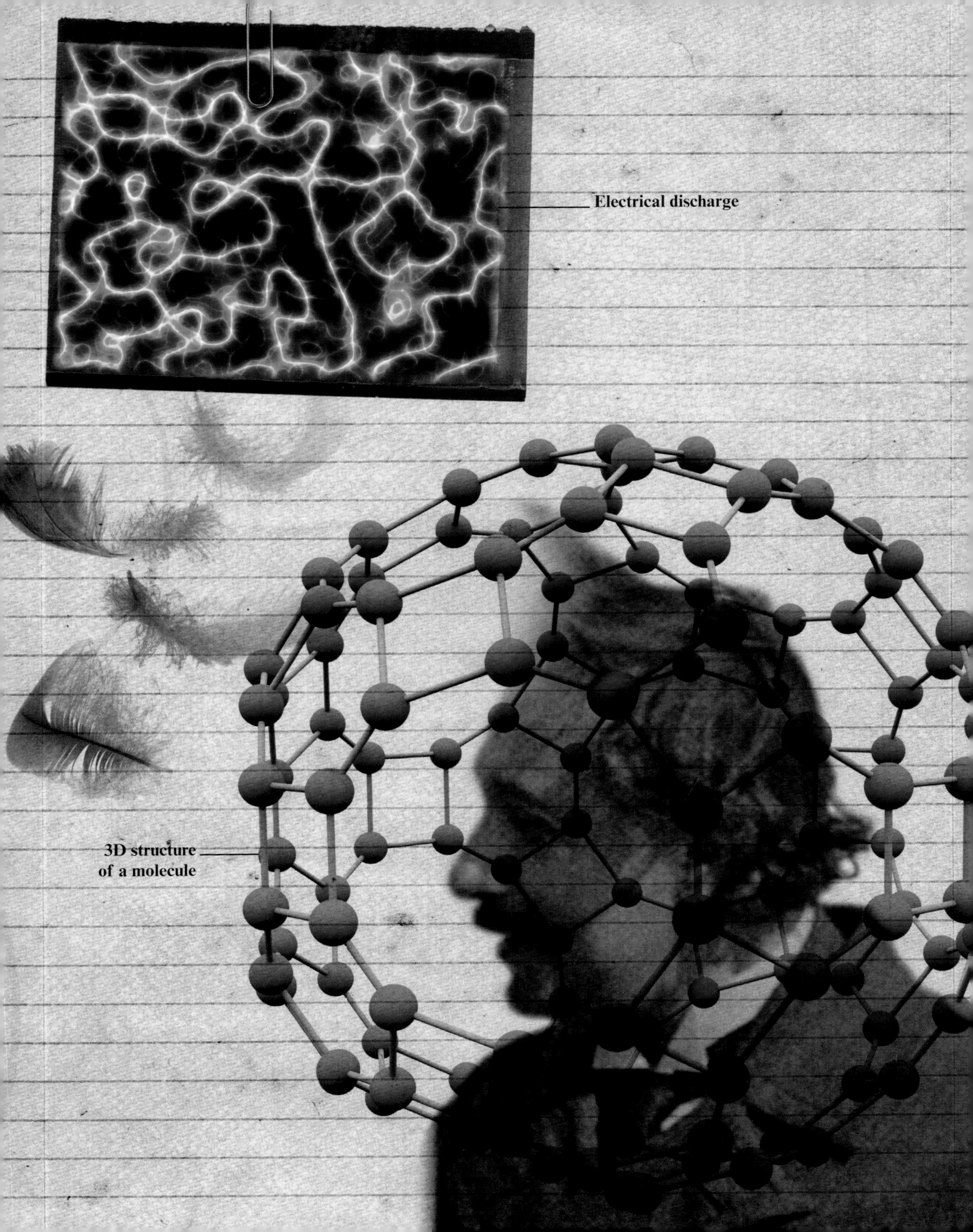
Electrical discharge
3D structure
of a molecule

Einstein's Philosophy

A picture is worth...

From an early age, Einstein liked to think in pictures. His **visual insights**, and the intuition they afforded him, were responsible for many of his early breakthroughs. The germ of the special theory was sown after Einstein imagined what it might be like to cycle alongside a beam of light. Similarly the way to the general theory became clear to Einstein after a thought experiment led him to the **equivalence principle**. Mathematics, the favorite tool of most **theoretical physicists**, had been just the means to the end for Einstein—the way to prove to his colleagues what he had already convinced himself of pictorially. Later on, however, Einstein seemed to forsake the visual approach—possibly after **brute-force mathematics** had helped him along the difficult home straight to the general theory. Some commentators have speculated that Einstein's departure from visual thinking is in part the reason why he made so few great discoveries in his later life.

Deductive reasoning

Einstein's preferred method of working was to use his **intuition** to arrive at grand, overarching principles and then calculate their consequences. For the special theory of relativity, these were the principle of relativity and the constancy of the speed of light. For the general theory, they were the equivalence principle and the revelation that gravity equates to curved geometry. Philosophers would interpret this by saying that Einstein favored **deductive reasoning**—he would take his principles and then deduce their consequences. This is in contrast to inductive reasoning—the **modus operandi** of many other scientists—who trawl through experimental data trying to spot trends and draw inferences from them.

Positivism

The young Einstein was a confirmed "**positivist**"—he was only interested in the observable aspects of nature. He had no interest in theories that could not be tested experimentally, which is perhaps what in part led him to reject ideas such as Newton's concept of **absolute space**. He later became more relaxed in this regard, however, possibly as a by-product of his ongoing war against quantum mechanics, in which he became a supporter of an alternative model known as "**hidden variable theory**." Until the 1960s, this theory was considered untestable.

3-second Brief

Want to know how to think like Einstein? Intuition, thought experiments, logical deduction, and the power of hard evidence were the main principles that guided him.

Related Thoughts

see also

FOUNDATIONS OF THE SPECIAL THEORY
page 74

FOUNDATIONS OF THE GENERAL THEORY
page 80

BIGGEST BLUNDERS
page 104

"The man of science is a poor philosopher."

Dampfmaschinchen denken, das
Du mir mitbrachtest, als Du
einmal von Russland kamst.
Es hat so ausgesehen:

Kannst Du Dich noch daran erinnern?
Dann, als Du in München mit
Deiner schlanken und schelmischen
jungen Frau bei uns warst, und
endlich, als ich Dich nach langen
Jahren, kurz vor der Verheiratung
Deiner Susanne in Antwerpen

Biggest Blunders

Hidden variables

Einstein's biggest **blooper**—and one he would never admit to—was his reluctance to believe the interpretation of quantum theory. One version of it that he did have time for was called "hidden variable theory." Einstein hated the indeterminate nature of ordinary quantum theory, with seemingly identical quantum systems capable of behaving in radically different ways. But in hidden variable theory there are parameters that make seemingly identical quantum systems different—the parameters are just hidden from view, so creating the **illusion** that the system is indeterminate. Irish physicist **John Bell** subsequently showed that if hidden variable theory was correct, then certain mathematical inequalities had to be obeyed. But in 1982, French physicist **Alain Aspect** performed a landmark experiment, proving that Bell's inequalities are violated. Hidden variable theory is thus wrong.

The cosmological constant

Shortly after the general theory of relativity was published in 1915, Einstein applied it to the Universe at large to see what its implications were for cosmology. He soon found a problem. His equations seemed to be telling him that the Universe shouldn't be static—it must either expand or contract. At the time, **astronomical observations** suggested that the Universe really was static, and so Einstein introduced a fudge factor—called the "cosmological constant"—into his theory that would effectively cancel gravity at long range and thus hold the Universe still. When astronomers discovered in the late 1920s that the Universe really is **expanding** Einstein was understandably gutted, declaring the cosmological constant to be the "**biggest blunder**" of his scientific career. That was another mistake as there's recently been a great resurgence of interest in it.

The Big Bang

Even though Einstein would later become sympathetic to the idea that the Universe could be created from nothing, he was initially **repelled** by the idea. Later known as the Big Bang theory, it was first proposed in 1927 by Belgian physicist **Georges Lemaître** based on calculations made using the general theory. Einstein's objection to it was that the Universe would have to spring from a singularity where gravitational forces become infinite, much like the singularities thought to lie at the centers of black holes. Einstein believed such singularities to be unphysical. It later became clear that the **singularity problem** could be removed, but doing so demanded recourse to Einstein's other great bugbear of modern physics: quantum theory.

3-second Brief

Like everyone, Einstein made mistakes. He refused to accept quantum theory, for which evidence is now overwhelming, and missed the chance to predict that space is expanding.

Related Thoughts

see also
BLACK HOLES
page 92
MODERN COSMOLOGY
page 138

"Anyone who has never made a mistake has never tried anything new."

Timeline

1901
Einstein publishes his first ever scientific paper. It concerns the way liquids rise up narrow tubes—called "capillary rise."

1905
The miracle year, in which Einstein published four research papers, each of them revolutionary. Two of the papers set out the special theory of relativity.

1915
It takes Einstein a further 10 years to generalize relativity to include gravity and accelerated motion. But he succeeds and publishes the "general theory of relativity."

1917
Einstein adds the "cosmological constant" to his equations of the general theory of relativity so as to prevent the Universe from expanding. Cosmic expansion is discovered 12 years later.

1917
Application of the general theory of relativity to the Universe prompts Einstein to make the first suggestion that space on large scales could be curved into a sphere.

1919
British astronomer Sir Arthur Eddington makes the historic eclipse observations that prove the general theory of relativity to be correct. Einstein becomes an overnight celebrity.

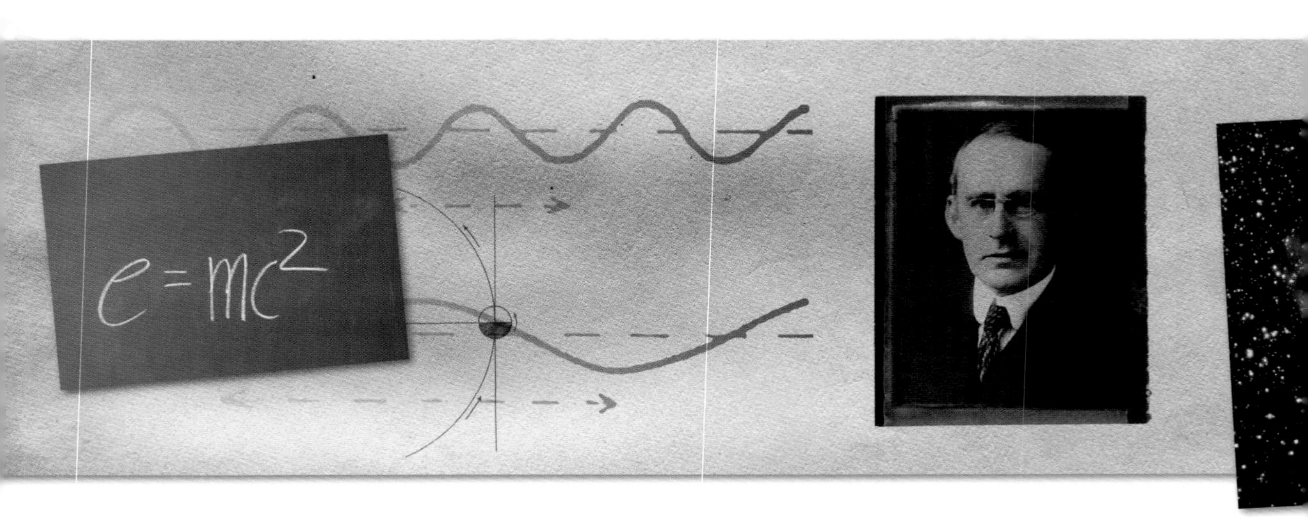

1923
At his Nobel lecture (having won the 1921 Nobel Prize in Physics) Einstein declares his intention next to find a theory that will unify gravity and electromagnetism.

1924
Indian physicist Satyendra Nath Bose formulates a theory of light that Einstein adapts—leading to astonishing predictions about the bulk properties of matter.

1926
In a letter to German physicist Max Born, Einstein makes his famous remark that "God does not play dice," referring to his disbelief in the uncertainty of quantum physics.

1930
Einstein is granted a US patent for a new design of refrigerator that requires no electricity. But it is quickly superseded by efficient modern designs.

1935
Einstein and Nathan Rosen suggest that it might be possible to travel through some kinds of black holes, which later become known as "wormholes."

1935
The idea that pairs of quantum particles can remain linked is ridiculed by Einstein, Nathan Rosen, and Boris Podolsky. But it turns out to be true, leading to quantum entanglement, a pillar of modern quantum theory.

Glossary

Atoms The basic constituents of naturally occurring chemical elements.

Black hole An object that is so dense its gravitational field will not allow light to escape.

Brownian motion The jittering motion of particles, such as specks of dust suspended in the air, which Einstein explained in 1905.

Cosmological constant A number added to the equations of the general theory to prevent a conclusion that the Universe is expanding.

Event horizon The outer surface of a black hole.

Frame dragging Einstein's general theory of relativity predicts that massive, rotating objects should drag space and time around with them like a spoon in molasses.

General theory of relativity Einstein's magnum opus theory, which equates the force of gravity to the curvature of space and time.

Gravitational lensing When the gravity of massive objects bends light beams and brings them to a focus, just like a glass lens.

Gravitational waves Ripples in space given out by time-varying gravitational fields, such as the gravitational field of a supernova explosion. They are one of the last untested predictions of the general theory of relativity.

Hidden variables A defunct interpretation of quantum theory in which quantum randomness is an illusion, generated by a set of variables that behave deterministically and yet are hidden from view.

Length contraction Phenomenon of the special theory of relativity that means a stationary observer will see moving objects get shorter.

Light bending Bending of starlight around the Sun predicted by the general theory, confirmed in 1919.

Molecules The basic building blocks of a chemical compound, made by bonding together atoms.

Perihelion precession The closest point of Mercury's orbit around the Sun—the perihelion—moves, or "precesses," over time. The general theory of relativity predicted the effect and its magnitude.

Photoelectric effect Einstein's theoretical description explaining how sunlight falling on a metal produces an electric current.

Photons The fundamental particles of light.

Quantum spin A property of subatomic particles predicted by applying the special theory of relativity to quantum theory.

Quantum theory The physics of the very small, in which energy is "quantized"—coming only in discrete chunks.

Quantum uncertainty A principle of quantum theory that states it is impossible to know everything about a subatomic particle at once.

Scalar A mathematical quantity with magnitude specified by one number. Mass of an object is an example.

Simultaneity Einstein said two events simultaneous to one observer are not simultaneous to another observer moving differently.

Special theory of relativity Einstein's theory of relative motion between objects traveling at close to the speed of light.

Tensor A mathematical quantity consisting of a matrix of numbers, used for transforming the values of vectors and scalars in physical theories.

Time dilation A moving clock ticks slower than one at rest, according to the special theory of relativity.

Unified field theory A theory tying together gravity and electromagnetism into one set of mathematical equations. Einstein spent much of his later life in pursuit of such a theory.

Vector A mathematical quantity that has both magnitude and direction, such as the speed and direction of water flowing in a stream.

United States 8c
EINSTEIN

Chapter 3

Influence

Electronics

GPS

Next time that computerized voice from the dashboard stops you from losing your way, remember to thank Albert Einstein. The Global Positioning System (GPS) works using a constellation of **satellites** in orbit around the Earth. Each satellite beams out a super-precise time signal (accurate to about a billionth of a second). A GPS unit on the ground receives the **time signals** from several satellites and compares them with its own internal clock to work out each satellite's distance. Because the satellite's orbital positions are well-known, this then pinpoints the GPS unit's location on the **Earth's surface**. However, the satellites are moving, so their clocks slow down according to relativistic time dilation. That's not all. Because the clock on the GPS unit is deeper in the Earth's gravitational field than the clocks on the satellites, it runs slower because of the general theory of relativity. Both these effects have to be corrected, and Einstein's theory provided the tools to do it.

3-second Brief

Einstein would have benefited from owning a GPS unit—his sense of direction was hopeless. Fitting, then, that it's his own theory of relativity that makes these devices possible.

Semiconductors

Semiconductors are materials through which the flow of electrical current can be precisely regulated. They are the basis of the modern **microchips** inside everything from your computer to your MP3 player. Semiconductors come in two different types, known as N-type (in which electric current is carried by negatively charged electrons) and P-type (in which the current is carried by positively charged "holes" in a sea of electrons). The motions of these charge carriers through a semiconducting material are described by the **Einstein relation**, developed as part of Einstein's research into **Brownian motion**.

Related Thoughts

see also
THE SPECIAL THEORY OF RELATIVITY
page 76
CONSEQUENCES OF THE GENERAL THEORY
page 86

Spintronics

Modern computers record information by storing electrical charge in semiconductor microchips. The information is recorded in **binary form**—as an array of 1s and 0s—with a charge representing a 1 and no charge representing a 0. But in the 1980s, physicists realized there was an **alternative** way to store data—using a property of subatomic particles called quantum spin. Broadly analogous to everyday spin, it is direct result of Einstein's special theory of relativity. Quantum spin comes in one of two states, labeled "up" and "down," and these two spin states can be used to store binary data—doing so more efficiently than devices based on charge. This **technology** is called spintronics.

"I'm on my way home and I've forgotten where my house is."

PHONE CALL TO DEPARTMENTAL SECRETARY IN PRINCETON

GPS
satellite

Energy

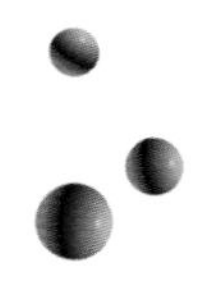

Solar panels

When Einstein discovered how metals exposed to **sunlight** can produce an electric current, he paved the way for the modern revolution in solar power. **Solar panels** work by a related phenomenon, called the photovoltaic effect. When a photon of sunlight falls on a junction of N- and P-type semiconductors it not only ejects an electron, as in the photoelectric effect, but also leaves a positively charged hole where the electron was. The electron is attracted toward the positively charged P-type material while the hole is attracted to the N-type material. Since positive charge flowing one way is the same as negative charge flowing in the opposite direction, the two effects reinforce one another to create an **electric current**.

3-second Brief

Scientists anticipate that oil and coal are running out. Just as well that Einstein's discoveries have given us alternative power sources for this century—and many more to come.

Nuclear power

Approximately 14 percent of the world's energy needs are now met by harnessing the energy locked away inside the heart of the atom. An atom is made of a cloud of electrons surrounding a central nucleus. In the 1930s, physicists discovered how to break **atomic nuclei** in two. But when they did this, they noticed something strange—the combined masses of the two halves was less than the mass of the original nucleus. Where had the missing mass gone? Einstein provided the answer through his famous formula $E=mc^2$, which says that mass and energy are equivalent. It meant that the tiny mass deficit created by splitting the atom is in fact being turned into energy. And indeed, this is the basis for **nuclear fission**, the process by which all **nuclear power stations** now operate.

Related Thoughts

see also
ELECTROMAGNETISM
page 72
ELECTRONICS
page 112

Antimatter

In the future, energy could be generated from antimatter. This is matter in which certain properties, such as electric charge, are reversed. So, for example, negatively charged electron particles have positively charged **antiparticles** (positrons) that are identical to the electron in every other way. When a particle of matter encounters its antiparticle, the mass of both gets converted entirely into energy. Antimatter was another prediction that arose from applying Einstein's laws of relativity to quantum theory when British physicist Paul Dirac built a relativistic equation of motion for electron particles in 1928. Although **costly** to manufacture, some scientists have suggested that antimatter could be mined from space—where the strong magnetic fields of some planets, such as **Jupiter**, will attract it. Tiny amounts of antimatter are used today in positron emission tomography (PET) medical scanners.

"Very small amounts of mass may be converted into a very large amount of energy."

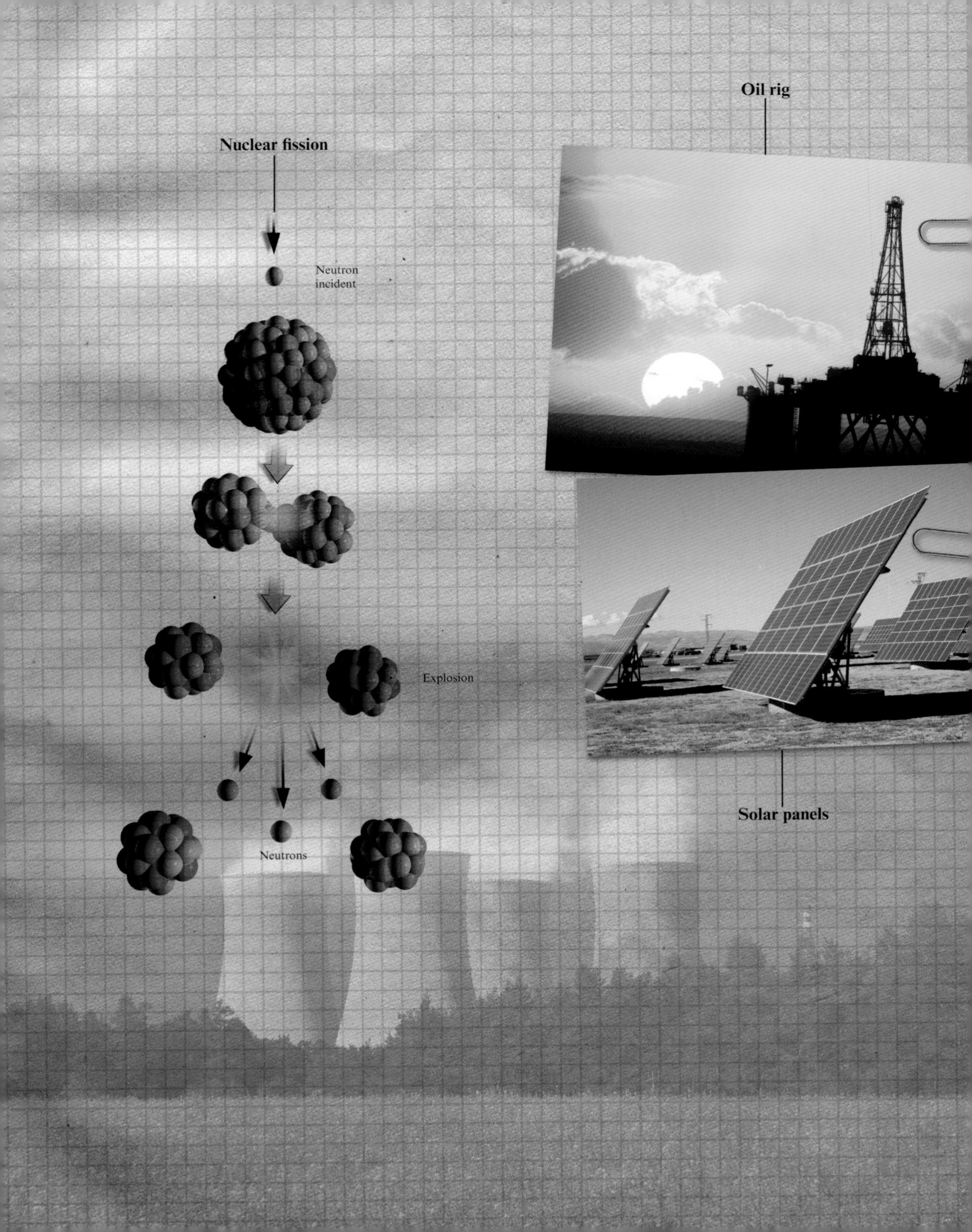

Oil rig

Nuclear fission

Neutron incident

Explosion

Neutrons

Solar panels

Lasers

Fiber optics

Lasers are an essential component in fiber-optic communications. Ordinary wires transmit data as pulses of electrical current. Fiber optics use a **laser** to encode signals as a rapid sequence of light pulses that are then fired down a narrow strand of plastic or glass. This set-up allows data to be transmitted at staggering speeds—up to 100 billion binary digits (or "bits") per second. This is thousands of times quicker than standard copper wires, with the added benefit that **fiber optics** are not prone to electromagnetic interference or resistive losses, where an electrical signal loses power as it heats the metal it's traveling through. It's likely fiber optics will find further applications in the future, ferrying data around inside superfast information processors called **quantum computers**.

Optical media

Without lasers, there would be no music CDs and no DVD or Blu-ray disks on which to view high-quality movies. These disks are a way of recording **information** that's become known as optical data storage. It works by pressing tiny pits into the surface of a **reflective disk**. The pits are separated by raised plateaus, or "lands," and the precise spacing between each pit and land is what encodes the data, as a sequence of binary 1s and 0s. To read it back, a laser is shone on the disk as it spins. When the laser beam falls on either a pit or a land it gets reflected back to a light sensor—this corresponds to a bit value of 0. But whenever the disk surface switches from pit to land or vice-versa the reflected beam momentarily **misses the light sensor** and a binary 1 is read off instead.

Nuclear fusion

Modern nuclear power stations rely on the principle of nuclear fission—**splitting heavy atoms** apart in order to liberate energy. But there is another form of nuclear power—fusion—where energy is generated instead by joining together lighter atoms, such as hydrogen. Because **hydrogen** is plentiful on Earth (it's found in water), and because fusion is much safer than fission, it's regarded by many as a power source for the future. One practical problem, however, is creating the high temperatures—tens of millions of degrees—needed to kick-start the process. A solution now being actively researched is that this could be done using powerful laser beams to heat and compress pellets of **fusion fuel**.

3-second Brief

Einstein's work on the emission of light by atoms leads American physicist Charles Townes to invent the laser. It turns out to have one or two applications.

Related Thoughts

see also
NATURE OF LIGHT
page 68
ENERGY
page 114
QUANTUM ENTANGLEMENT
page 122

"A brilliant idea dawned on me about radiation absorption and emission. It will interest you."

LETTER TO HIS FRIEND MICHELE BESSO

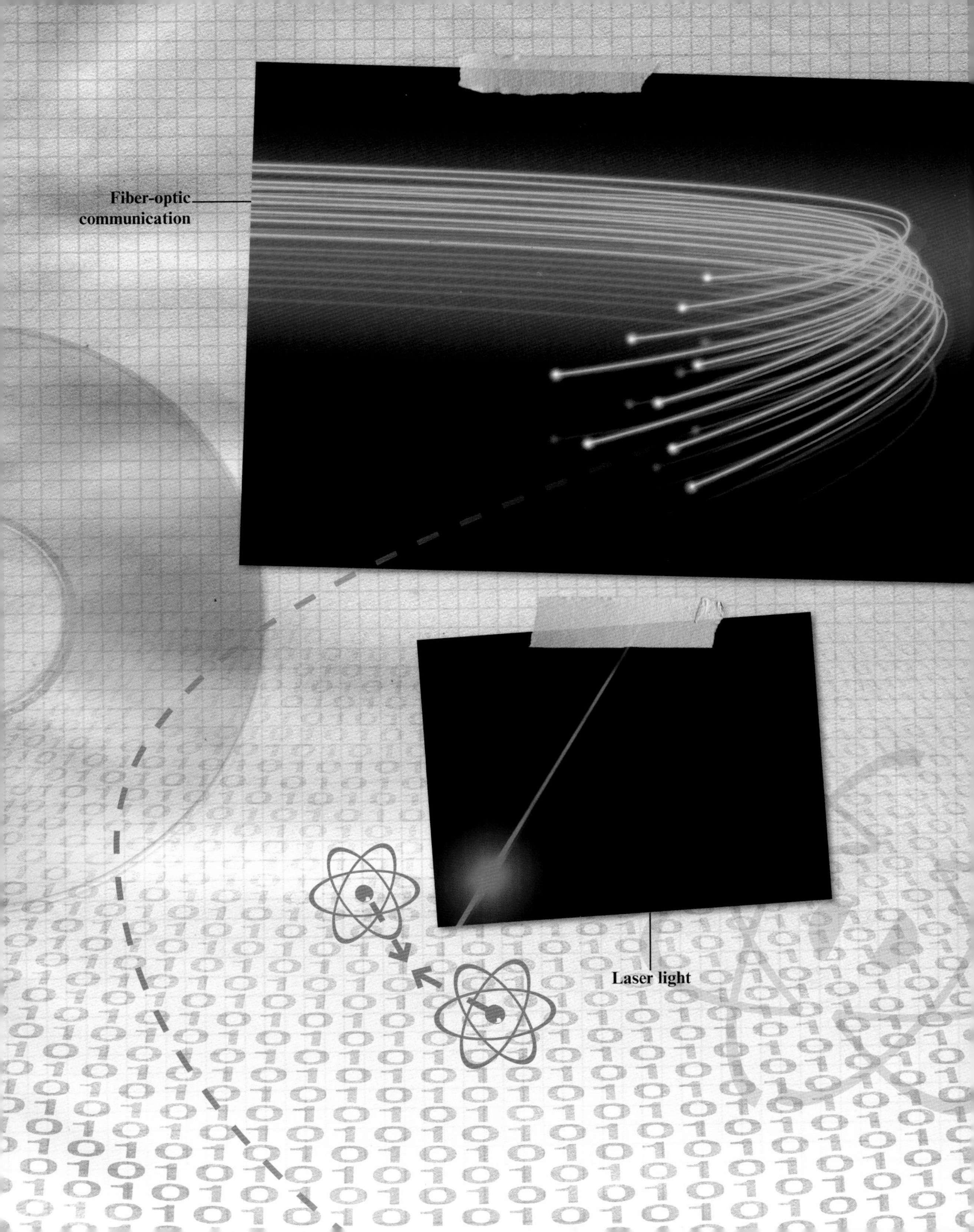
Fiber-optic communication
Laser light

Modern Unification Theories

Electroweak theory

There are four fundamental forces in nature—gravity, electromagnetism, and the strong and weak nuclear forces that dominate inside the nuclei of atoms. In 1968, physicists **Steven Weinberg, Abdus Salam**, and **Sheldon Glashow** succeeded in unifying two of these—electromagnetism and the weak nuclear force. In their model, known as the electroweak theory, electromagnetism and the weak force are just different aspects of the same physics. Experiments in particle accelerators in the 1970s tallied with the theory's predictions, leading to Weinberg, Salam, and Glashow receiving the 1979 **Nobel Prize** in Physics. And yet there is still one piece of the theory missing—the elusive **Higgs boson**, which modern accelerator machines are now hunting for.

Supersymmetry

Subatomic particles are divided into two broad families, known as fermions and bosons. The groups are partitioned according to the value of a quantum property known as **spin**. Each particle's spin is specified by a number which can either be an integer, such as 1, 2, 3, and so on (these are the bosons), or a half integer, i.e. 1/2, 3/2, 5/2 (these are the fermions). The idea of supersymmetry is that for every boson there is a counterpart fermion, and vice-versa. If the theory is correct, then during the early Universe all of these "**superpartners**" existed, until so-called symmetry-breaking events whittled them down to leave just the small selection of particles we see today. Supersymmetry—or SUSY as it's sometimes known—is appealing to physicists because it irons out some of the **mathematical bugs** of candidate unification theories.

String theory

String theory is a candidate unified theory of particle physics—but without the **particles**. Instead it deals tiny vibrating "strings" of energy. The theory was first put forward in the late 1960s as a possible way to remove the "divergences," **unrealistic infinities** in the values of physical quantities (such as particle masses), that were thrown up by other unified models. Some physicists believed these divergences arose from modeling particles as points of zero size, when in reality they must have some degree of physical extent. Like the earlier Kaluza-Klein unified model, string theory requires extra spacetime dimensions, six of them, bringing the total dimensionality of our Universe to 10. Some versions of **string theory** also build in supersymmetry, to give "superstrings."

3-second Brief

Einstein spent a good deal of his life trying to formulate a unified description of the forces of nature. He ultimately failed. Physicists today are still trying.

Related Thoughts

see also

CONSEQUENCES OF THE SPECIAL THEORY
page 78

UNIFIED FIELD THEORY
page 100

PARTICLE ACCELERATORS
page 120

"The mind striving after unification cannot be satisfied that two fields should exist which, by their nature, are quite independent."

Particle Accelerators

Quest for a unified theory

Despite the best attempts of scientists to deduce a unified model encompassing all four forces of nature, at present all their theories remain **unproven**—in fact, there's no compelling evidence that physics is even unified at all. To try and get a better handle on the problem, physicists use particle accelerators, machines with **powerful magnets** that whiz electrically charged particles up to near the speed of light and then crash them into one another. Studying the fragments that fly out from the **collisions** offers insights into how the particle world really works.

Large Hadron Collider

The most powerful particle accelerator in the world is the Large Hadron Collider at the CERN laboratory on the Swiss-French border. The accelerator takes the form of a giant underground ring, **16.8 miles (27km)** in circumference, around which particles circulate, gathering speed. At top speed, the particles traverse the loop 11,000 times every second—just 9.8 feet (3m) per second shy of lightspeed. The number of particles circulating at any one time is tiny, small enough to fit inside a grain of sand, and yet at this speed the energy they pack is equivalent to the **explosive force** of nearly 400lbs (180kg) of TNT. Among its many objectives, the LHC is searching for particles predicted by supersymmetry, the extra dimensions essential to unification models such as string theory, and the Higgs boson particle required for **electroweak unification**.

The Higgs boson

A key objective of the LHC is to try and find the Higgs boson particle—the only missing element of the electroweak theory. The particle was predicted in the early 1960s by British physicist **Peter Higgs**. His idea was that Higgs bosons pervade the whole of space, and that it is the interactions with this field of particles which gives all other matter in the Universe its **mass**. This mechanism is essential in the electroweak theory in order to explain why the particles of the electromagnetic field (photons) are massless, while those of the weak interaction (known as the W and Z) are among the heaviest known. However, finding evidence for the Higgs boson is difficult. This is because its own mass is so high—at least one-and-a-half times the mass of a W particle. As Einstein demonstrated, mass and energy are equivalent, so creating very high-mass particles requires a very high-energy particle accelerator. And that's where the **LHC** comes in.

3-second Brief

The special theory of relativity is the physics of moving fast. And nothing on Earth moves faster than the particles inside giant experimental machines known as accelerators.

Related Thoughts

see also
UNIFIED FIELD THEORY
page 100
MODERN UNIFICATION THEORIES
page 118

"Look deep into nature, and then you will understand everything better."

Simulation of Higgs boson decaying

Large Hadron Collider

Quantum Entanglement

Secure communication

Einstein first invoked quantum entanglement, using its seeming absurdity to argue that quantum theory is incorrect. Now it's known to be very real. A pair of quantum particles that are entangled remain **linked** no matter how far apart they are—take them to opposite sides of the cosmos, wiggle one and the other wiggles back. In 1984, researchers at IBM used this as the basis for a **quantum communication system** that's secure against eavesdroppers. Quantum uncertainty means an eavesdropper trying to listen in on a message sent down an entangled channel will alter the message and thus reveal their presence. If the message is a **private encryption key**, that'll be used to encode future messages securely, then quantum communication ensures that this key is only seen by the intended recipients—if an eavesdropper is detected the key is canceled and a new one sent out.

Teleportation

In 1997, experimental physicists at the **University of Innsbruck** in Austria used quantum entanglement to teleport a subatomic particle across their laboratory. For years it was believed that the possibility of teleportation was ruled out by quantum uncertainty, which prevents you measuring the exact state of a subatomic particle. But entanglement lets you transmit information that you haven't measured. Take two entangled particles, A and B, and move them far apart. A third particle, C, interacting with A transfers information about its state to A which then, by entanglement, is "**teleported**" to B. A fourth particle, D, interacting with B can now be placed into exactly the same state as the original C. This scheme has now been verified over distances of up to **10 miles (16km)**.

Quantum computers

Teleportation will be used to transfer information inside "quantum computers." These are machines, currently at the **experimental stage**, that store and manipulate data using quantum processes rather than the classical (or non-quantum) laws by which today's **computers** operate. Whereas a classical computer processes information as bits, binary digits that can take the value of either 1 or 0, a quantum computer uses "qubits" that can be both 1 and 0 at the same time. This is possible because quantum systems can be in two states simultaneously. A quantum byte, made of eight qubits, can be in **256 different states** at the same time—all of which can then be processed in a single quantum operation.

3-second Brief

Einstein's derisory musings on quantum theory fail to recognize that it will pave the way for uncrackable codes, *Star Trek*-style teleporters, and computers that make the best of today look like slide rules.

Related Thoughts

see also
THE QUANTUM WORLD
page 96

"Physics should represent a reality in time and space, free from spooky action at a distance."

Relativity Paradoxes

The twin paradox

Imagine two twin sisters on Earth. If one gets aboard a **spaceship** and flies off for several years at close to the speed of light, then upon her return she will find that she's **aged less** than the twin who stayed home the whole time—because of the time dilation effect of the special theory. But Einstein's principle of relativity says all reference frames are equivalent. In that case, you should equally be able to view the whole thing from the perspective of the space traveler. Then it's her sister and the Earth that appear to fly off at near lightspeed. In which case, shouldn't the terrestrial twin be the one who comes back **younger**? This is the twin paradox.

3-second Brief

From a common-sense perspective, many of the outcomes of relativity seem at first paradoxical. The solution is simple: leave your common sense at the door.

The barn-pole paradox

Imagine a pole vaulter who's capable of running at close to **lightspeed**. Relative to a stationary observer the vaulter's pole gets shorter, because of length contraction. Now imagine that the vaulter runs through an **open-ended barn**. The observer notices that even though the pole is normally longer than the barn, the shortening means that it's now the **same length**—so that the doors at both ends could be shut for a split second. But in the vaulter's own frame, the pole is unshortened and thus still longer than the barn—so how can the doors be shut?

Related Thoughts

see also
FOUNDATIONS OF THE SPECIAL THEORY
page 74
THE SPECIAL THEORY OF RELATIVITY
page 76

Paradox lost

The resolution to the twin paradox lies in the fact that the special theory actually only demands non-accelerating reference frames to be equivalent. And the spaceship has to **accelerate**, first to high speed, then stop, and then accelerate again for the return journey, and stop once more. This creates an **asymmetry** that means the two frames—Earth and spaceship—are not equivalent. The upshot is that the twin on the spaceship is indeed the one who comes back younger. The barn-pole conundrum is resolved by remembering that in relativity events that are simultaneous to one observer are not necessarily simultaneous to another. So whereas the stationary observer sees both doors shut at the same time, the vaulter sees the door ahead of him shut and open again before the front of the pole reaches it, while the door behind only shuts once the back end of the pole has passed. And so there is **no paradox**.

"A new idea comes suddenly and in a rather intuitive way. But intuition is nothing but the outcome of earlier intellectual experience."

Is Relativity Wrong?

Scalar-tensor theories

The success of the general theory of relativity hasn't stopped others from trying to improve on it. In 1961, American physicists **Robert Dicke** and **Carl Brans** put forward a theory that supplements the tensor field of the general theory of relativity (specified by a matrix of numbers at each point in space) with a scalar field, a new component of gravity that's specified by just a single additional number at each point. **Experimental tests** have now all but ruled out the validity of the Brans-Dicke idea, however it set the scene for a flood of similar models known as **scalar-tensor theories**. They are motivated by the appearance of scalar fields in many attempts to unify the forces of nature.

TeVeS

There's another kind of field that lies in between scalars and tensors—a "vector" field is given by a row of numbers at each point in space, one number for each dimension of the space. For example, the speed of a **flowing liquid** is a vector field, with three numbers at each point within the liquid giving its speed and direction in each of the three dimensions of space. In 2004, physicist **Jacob Bekenstein**, at the Hebrew University of Jerusalem, added a vector component to gravity to make a so-called **tensor-vector-scalar theory**, or "TeVeS" as it's known. Bekenstein argues that his theory removes the need for "dark matter" in the Universe—invisible material in space, the presence of which has thus far been inferred purely from its gravitational effect on bright objects. He adds that TeVeS passes other experimental tests. However, other physicists are skeptical, and the theory remains **contentious**.

Quantum gravity

Most physicists agree that the general theory of relativity cannot be the **last word** on gravity. That's because it takes no account of quantum theory, the branch of physics governing the behavior of the very small. The general theory of relativity describes the Universe accurately today, but that can't always have been the case. Astronomers know that **space is expanding**. Trace that expansion backward in time and there comes a point—about 13.7 billion years ago, according to best estimates—when the Universe itself was only the size of an atom, and so must have obeyed quantum laws. A theory of "quantum gravity" is thus needed to describe this **Big Bang** in which space and time began.

3-second Brief

Despite having passed every single experimental test that's been thrown at it, most scientists agree that the general theory of relativity must ultimately be wrong.

Related Thoughts

see also

THE GENERAL THEORY OF RELATIVITY
page 82

MODERN UNIFICATION THEORIES
page 118

"No amount of experimentation can ever prove me right; a single experiment can prove me wrong."

Big Bang

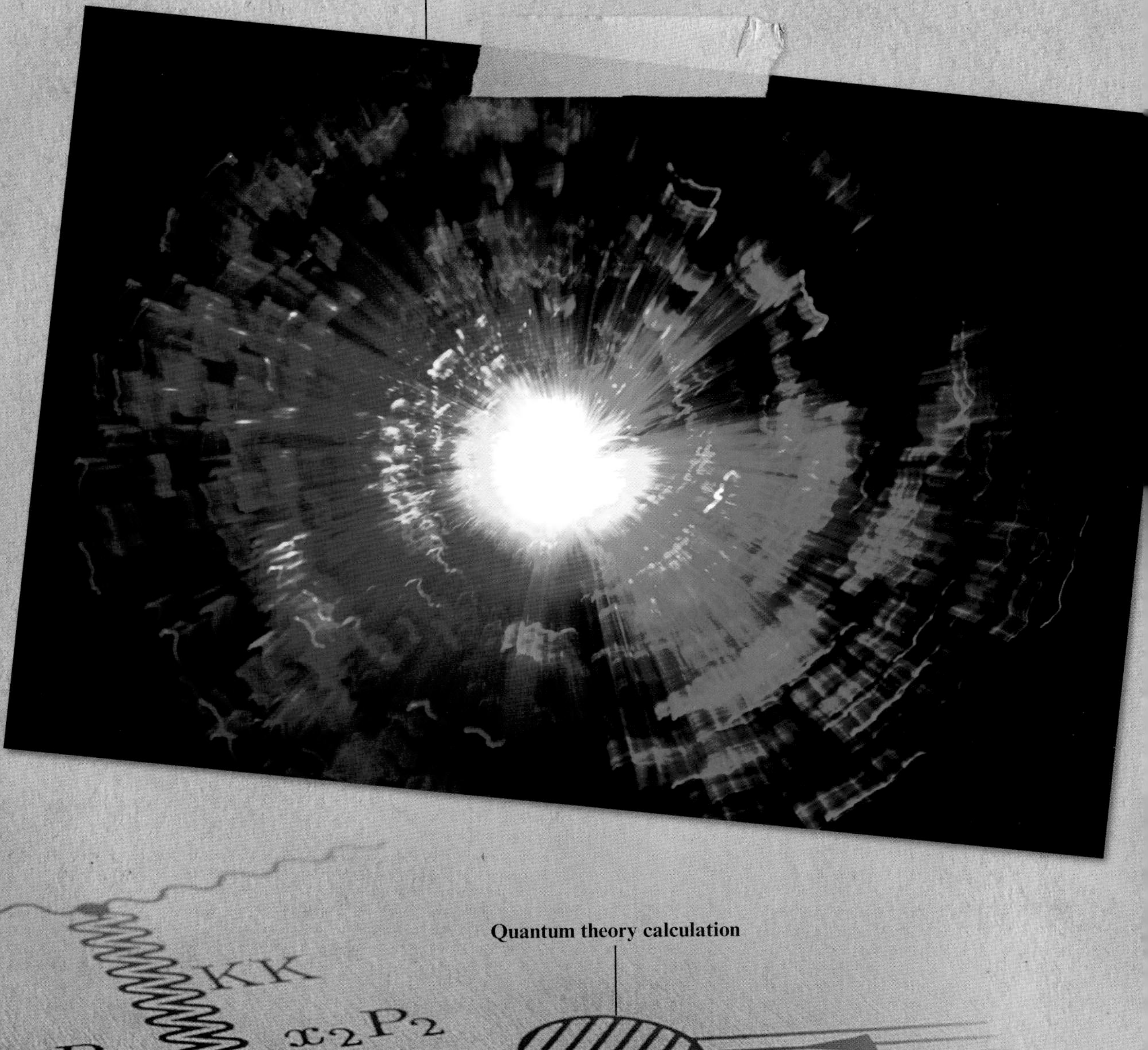

Quantum theory calculation

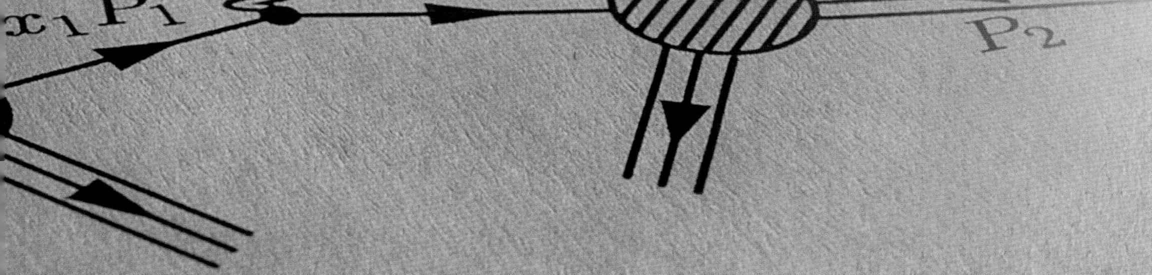

KK

$x_1 P_1$

$x_2 P_2$

P_2

Faster than Light

Tachyons

The special theory of relativity says nothing can travel faster than a **light beam**. Or does it? In fact, what is says is that nothing can cross the light barrier—from above or below. And because we, and the things we see around us, all **move slower** than light we interpret this barrier as an upper speed limit. But it also means any objects that are born moving faster than light can never go slower than lightspeed. Physicists have speculated that there could exist a kind of **subatomic particle** with exactly this property. It's called a tachyon. Because tachyons travel faster than light, you could never see one coming, but you'd see two images after it passed—one approaching and one receding. Experimental searches for them have been carried out, but none has ever been found.

Warp drive

In 1994, Mexican physicist **Miguel Alcubierre** proved mathematically that, while nothing can cross the light barrier in the flat space of the special theory of relativity, in the curved spacetime landscape of the general theory pretty much anything is possible. In particular, he worked out how to **bend and stretch** the space around a traveler so that in front of them it contracts rapidly while behind it expands at the same rate—thus sweeping the traveler along to their destination arbitrarily quickly. In the general theory of relativity, space bends according to the matter placed within it. Sadly for *Star Trek* fans, Alcubierre's aptly named "warp drive" requires planet-size masses of a kind of matter so weird it's known to physicists as "exotic matter," and has only been made in the **tiniest quantities** in laboratories.

Wormhole transport

Another way to go faster than light is to jump down a wormhole. This is a **tunnel through space** and time first suggested by Einstein and colleagues during the 1930s. In principle, at least, two regions of the Universe separated by **great distance** can be connected by a relatively short wormhole, which then acts as a quick dodge between them. If the wormhole is short enough, then a spacecraft traveling down it will arrive at its destination **faster than a beam of light** traveling through ordinary space—and so effectively the spacecraft travels faster than light. Like the warp drive, however, calculations suggest that wormholes require vast amounts of exotic matter in order to work.

3-second Brief

The cosmic speed limit that Einstein so carefully built into the special theory of relativity becomes a fading image in the rear-view mirror—thanks in part to Einstein himself.

Related Thoughts

see also
CONSEQUENCES OF THE SPECIAL THEORY
page 78
BLACK HOLES
page 92

"We all know that light travels faster than sound. That's why certain people appear bright until you hear them speak."

Wormhole

Time Travel

Into the future

Time travel is a well-worn staple of **science fiction**. Yet time travel in one direction—into the future—has already been proven possible. We are all travelers in time—heading into the **future** at the rate of one minute every minute, and Einstein's special theory of relativity showed how it's possible to speed this up. Time dilation says that if you travel very fast, then time for you slows down relative to a stationary observer, say back on Earth. Say you jet off in a spacecraft at 90 percent lightspeed, then for every minute that passes on your clock, two minutes will pass on a clock **back on Earth**—in other words you're traveling into the Earth's future at the rate of two minutes for one minute of your own time.

3-second Brief
Albert Einstein's theories don't just throw open the door for superfast travel across the gulf of space, but also backward through the mists of time...

Into the past

The tricky bit about time travel is getting back to your own time—no one is sure quite how you go about travelling into the past, or whether it's even **possible** to do so. Some physicists even hope it's beyond the realms of possibility because of the paradoxes thrown up by being able to travel back and **meet your younger self**. Others enthusiastically embrace the idea and have come up with all sorts of theoretical schemes for time machines by exploiting the freedom to curve time provided by the general theory of relativity. These include rotating Universes, wormholes, colliding lengths of energy known as "**cosmic strings**," and even one plan to build a time machine from swirling beams of light.

Related Thoughts
see also
THE SPECIAL THEORY OF RELATIVITY
page 76
IS TIME TRAVEL POSSIBLE?
page 132

Faster than time

One trick physicists use for constructing theoretical time machines is a mathematical property of relativity that means that any scheme for traveling faster than light can always be turned into a time machine by **observing** it from a moving frame of reference. The idea relies on the distorted view of "simultaneity" in relativity—where two events that appear simultaneous to one observer happen at different times when they are observed by another who's moving differently. Say it was possible to travel instantaneously between two points in space so that your departure and arrival at your destination happened **simultaneously**—that's definitely faster than light. Then to someone moving fast enough, simultaneity would make it possible for them to view your arrival as happening before your departure. In other words, they see you **travel into the past**.

"People like us, who believe in physics, know that the distinction between past, present, and future is only a stubbornly persistent illusion."

Is Time Travel Possible?

Time-travel paradoxes

The principal objection to time travel is the idea that you could go back into the past and **change history**. In extreme cases you could even call into question your own existence, as in the movie *Back to the Future*, in which the hero, Marty McFly, goes back to 1955 and inadvertently prevents the first chance encounter between his parents...which would mean that he wouldn't exist, and therefore wouldn't have been able to go back and stop his parents meeting, and so would exist, and so on. This is what's known as a "**time-travel paradox**." Another might be if the old and successful **William Shakespeare** went back in time and made a gift of all his great works to his younger self, who promptly copied them and published them. In this case, where did the inspiration for Shakespeare's plays actually come from?

Modern resolutions

Ever-resourceful physicists have come up with some neat dodges to get around these time-travel paradoxes. The first makes use of an idea from quantum theory—that our Universe is just one in a sprawling "**multiverse**" of parallel Universes. In this scheme, anyone going back in time actually travels into the past of one of these **parallel Universes**, and so leaves history intact in the Universe that they've come from. Another idea is known as "self consistency." This says that whenever the potential for a time-travel paradox arises, nature finds its own self-consistent course of events. Although that might sound rather arbitrary, scientists have found support for self consistency in calculations based on the so-called "principle of least action"—a key tenet at the heart of **theoretical physics**.

Chronology protection conjecture

These attempts to sidestep time-travel paradoxes have not impressed Professor **Stephen Hawking**, at the University of Cambridge, England. He is so convinced time travel cannot be possible that he's invented a scientific principle—called the "chronology protection conjecture"—which will, as he puts it, "keep the world safe for historians." No physical basis for the conjecture has yet been found. However, Hawking suspects that during the creation process any time machine would magnify tiny quantum energy fluctuations, which pervade all of space, making them **infinitely large**—and so destroying the time machine before anything can travel through it. Proving or disproving the conjecture, however, will have to wait for a working theory of **quantum gravity**.

3-second Brief

The realization that the general theory of relativity could permit travel through time triggers a raging debate as to whether time machines could ever exist in the real world.

Related Thoughts

see also
IS RELATIVITY WRONG?
page 126
TIME TRAVEL
page 130

"I never think of the future. It comes soon enough."

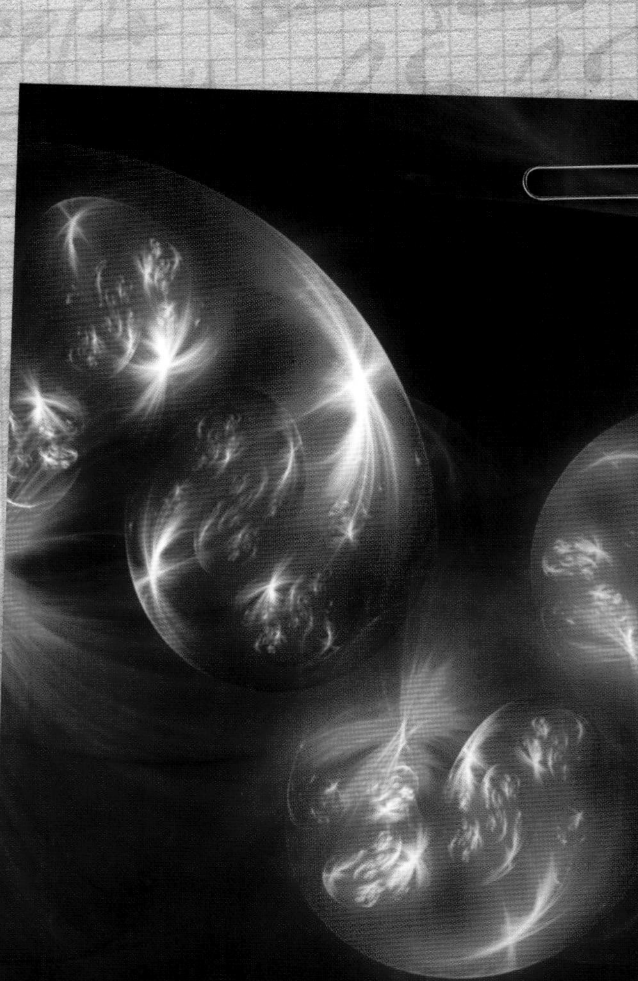

Visual interpretation of the "multiverse" of parallel Universes

New Black Holes

Charge and spin

German physicist **Karl Schwarzschild** wrote down the first mathematical description of a black hole in 1917. But physicists soon realized other, more complicated, varieties exist too. Hans Reissner and Gunnar Nordström were the first, when they modified Schwarzschild's solution to describe a **black hole** that's electrically charged. Reissner-Nordström black holes are particularly amenable to forming wormholes. In 1963, mathematician Roy Kerr solved Einstein's equation for a black hole that's **spinning**. Whereas the Reissner-Nordström solution amounted to just a small correction to Schwarzschild's, the Kerr solution was much more complex. Two years later, American physicist Ted Newman generalized the two solutions to describe a black hole with both charge and spin.

The Penrose process

The black holes of the Kerr solution turned out to have one very interesting property. In 1969, mathematician **Roger Penrose**, of Oxford University, realized that spinning black holes should drag space and time around with them, an example of **frame dragging**. In the extreme conditions around a black hole the effect is multiplied, so much so, Penrose showed, that it's possible to hitch a ride on the swirling space near the black hole and actually extract energy from it. He even imagined an advanced **extraterrestrial civilization** being able to establish itself near such a black hole and use its energy as a power source.

Hawking radiation

If Penrose's discovery was correct, then rotating black holes are no longer one-way funnels that continuously suck up matter and energy from the Universe—they can spit some back out, too. In 1974, another piece of research suggested this could be the case for all black holes. Stephen Hawking used quantum theory to show that black holes should actually emit a steady flux of particles and **radiation**. Hawking's idea stemmed from **quantum uncertainty**, whereby pairs of "virtual particles" can pop in and out of existence over very short time scales. Some of these particles will fall over the black hole's outer event horizon and be swallowed up, while their partners will have just enough energy to escape. These escaping particles make up the Hawking radiation. The amount of radiation given off is largest for small black holes, and can make the smallest ones **evaporate** away to nothing.

3-second Brief

The years 1960–1975 become known as the "Golden Age of General Relativity," partly due to a surge of theoretical discoveries concerning the nature of black holes.

Related Thoughts

see also
CONSEQUENCES OF THE GENERAL THEORY
page 86
BLACK HOLES
page 92
THE QUANTUM WORLD
page 96

"The most beautiful thing we can experience is the mysterious."

Roger Penrose
Black hole

Astrophysics

Neutron stars

It was soon to become clear that black holes aren't the only weird objects in the Universe. Black holes are thought to form during the death of a massive star in a colossal explosion known as a "**supernova**." Terrific pressures inside the star during the explosion are believed to compress its core, crushing it to such density that it has to become a black hole. That's because there's no force of nature strong enough to support the core against collapse. But when the exploding star weighs less than about 10 times the mass of the Sun, the force of the **implosion** is less, and quantum mechanical forces between neutron particles stabilize the core, forming an object called a "**neutron star**." It's extraordinarily dense, typically packing the mass of the Sun into a sphere just 6 miles (10km) across.

3-second Brief

Einstein's theories of relativity give scientists the tools to unpick the mysteries of deep space, shedding light on the death of stars and revealing invisible planets.

Microlensing

In 1936, Albert Einstein introduced the concept of **gravitational lensing**—the bending of light from distant galaxies by the gravity of intervening galaxies or clusters. But gravitational lensing can also take place on much smaller scales—for example, when **light from a star** is lensed by the gravity of a planet passing in front of it. This is known as "**microlensing**," and indeed, it's recognized as a method for detecting such small, dark objects that give off no light of their own. As a planet passes in front of a star it focuses the star's light, causing it momentarily to brighten. The first such microlensing event was observed by astronomers in 1993. The technique is now used to search for **extrasolar planets** and failed stars (known as brown dwarfs).

Related Thoughts

see also
THE SPECIAL THEORY OF RELATIVITY
page 76
EXTENDING THE GENERAL THEORY
page 90
BLACK HOLES
page 92

Cosmic-ray astronomy

Cosmic rays aren't "rays" at all. They are superfast **subatomic particles** from outer space that crash into the Earth's atmosphere. They carry an awful lot of energy—a single **cosmic ray** packs the same punch as a fast tennis serve, all crammed into a tiny particle. They are studied using ground-based particle detectors which pick up not the cosmic rays themselves but the debris from their collisions with gas atoms in the atmosphere, which filter down to the ground in so-called "**air showers**." These air-shower detectors are made possible by relativity. If it wasn't for relativistic time dilation, most of the fragments would have decayed away to nothing long before they reached the ground.

"We still do not know one thousandth of one percent of what nature has revealed to us."

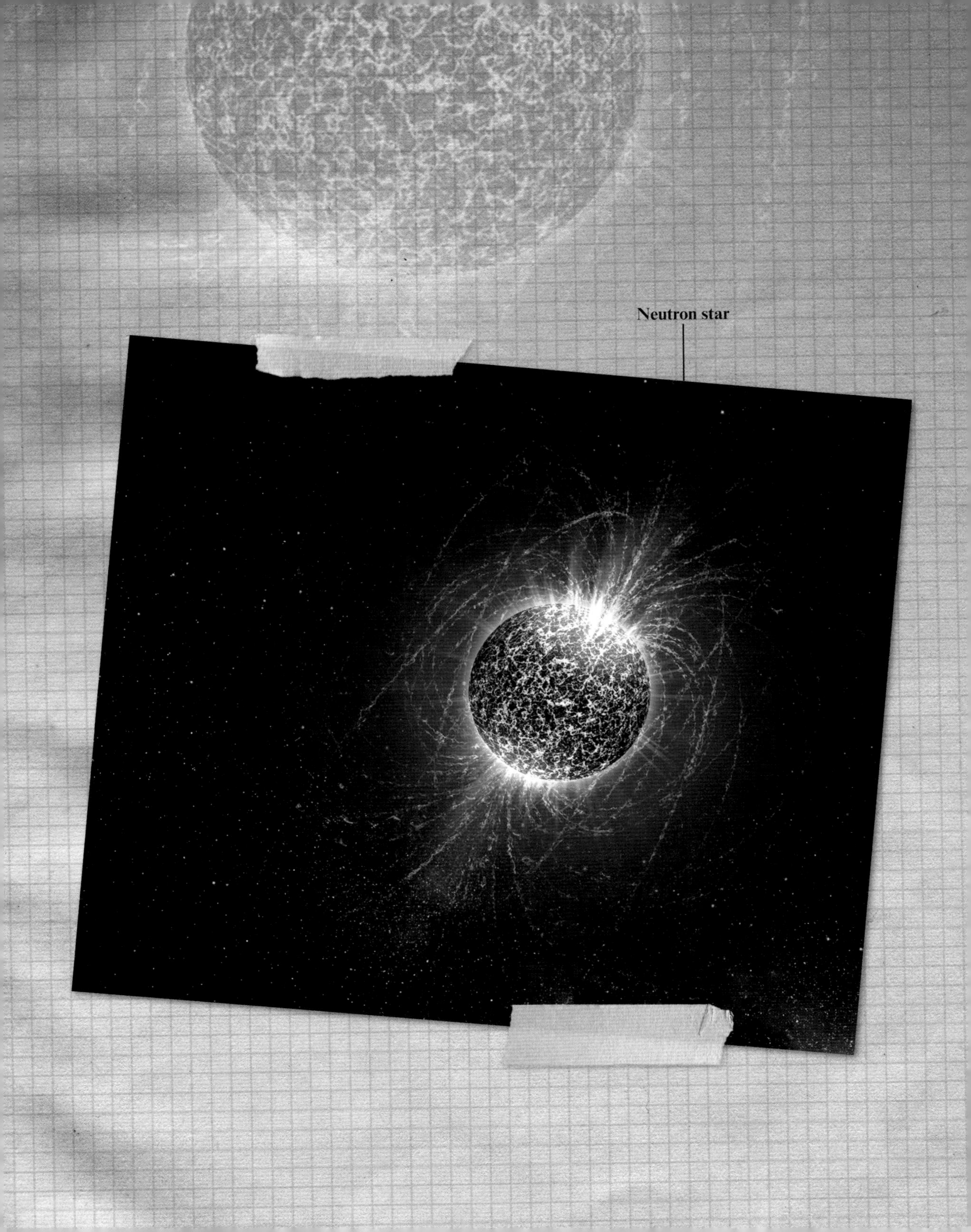
Neutron star

Modern Cosmology

Dark energy

In the 1920s, astronomers discovered that the Universe is expanding. Most theoreticians believed this expansion should be gradually slowing down, because of the gravitational pull of all the matter in the Universe. In the 1990s, however, **astronomical observations** suggested that distant galaxies aren't receding from us as fast as they should be, compared with galaxies closer to Earth. Because light travels at finite speed, the distant galaxies were being seen as they were when the Universe was younger—and so the observations suggested that the expansion of the Universe is actually **accelerating**. An invisible energy field pervading all of space—called "dark energy"—was posited as the cause of the expansion. Mathematically, it looks identical to the cosmological constant that Einstein first introduced and then discarded as his "biggest blunder." Dark energy is thought to comprise **74 percent** of the Universe's total mass-energy.

3-second Brief

Scientists take Einstein's musings on the Universe at large and run with them, yielding the possibility of superfast cosmic expansion and the idea that space looks like a donut.

Inflation

In fact, the cosmological constant had already been resurrected a few years earlier. During the 1970s, cosmologists noticed that several of the problems plaguing the **Big Bang theory** of the Universe—such as why opposite sides of the night sky look more or less the same—could be neatly solved if space had undergone a phase of **ultra-rapid expansion** during the first split-second after creation. This period of accelerated growth was called "inflation." If inflation really was a feature of our Universe, then it would have finished just 10^{-32} (one hundred-thousand-billion-billion-billionth) of a second after the Big Bang.

Related Thoughts

see also
COSMOLOGY
page 98
BIGGEST BLUNDERS
page 104

Cosmic topology

Einstein was the first to investigate the possibility that our Universe could be **spherical**—its space curved into a giant ball by the distorting effects of the general theory. Since then, cosmologists have realized that there are many possibilities for the overall shape of the cosmos. Space and time could be donut-shaped, twisted around like a **Möbius strip**, or knotted up into an even more complex form. Mathematicians call the study of such shapes "topology." Theoretical Universe models that have this wrap-around property—where you exit one side only to re-enter on the other—are known as "**multiply-connected Universes**." In 2003, astronomers from Paris Meudon Observatory found evidence that our Universe could be multiply-connected, resembling a 12-sided shape called a dodecahedron—the idea being that if you leave through one face, you reappear through the face opposite.

"We see a Universe marvelously arranged and obeying certain laws, but only dimly understand these laws."

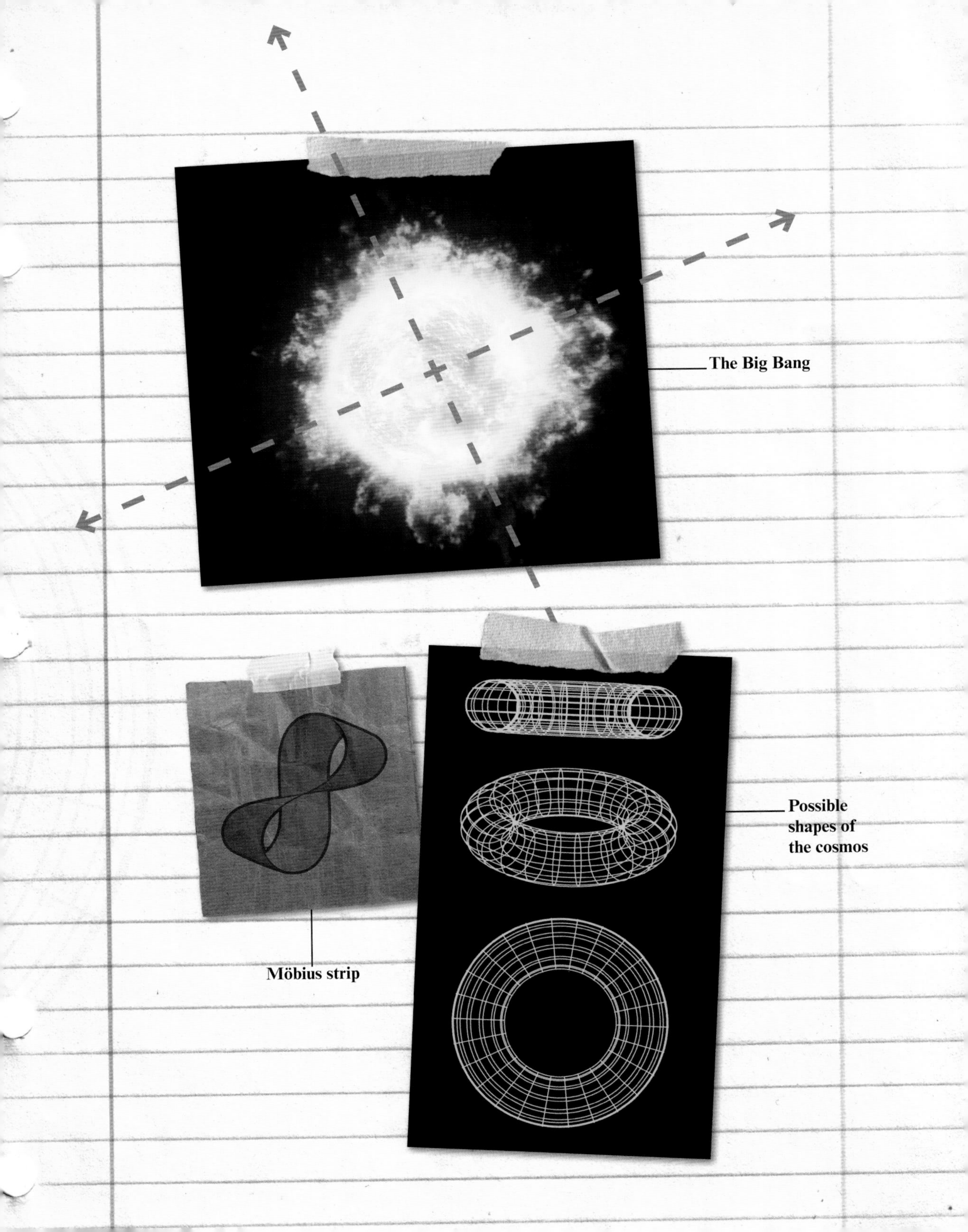
The Big Bang
Possible
shapes of
the cosmos
Möbius strip

Eponymous Discoveries

Asteroid Einstein

To any space enthusiast it's a privilege to have an asteroid named after you—but when you're someone who contributed as much to our understanding of the Universe as Einstein did, the honor is supreme. **Asteroid 2001 Einstein** was discovered in 1973 by Swiss astronomer Paul Wild. It orbits in the main belt, between Mars and Jupiter, and is part of the **Hungaria** family which sits on the innermost edge of the belt and orbits the Sun roughly once every 2.5 years. The science fiction author and futurologist Sir Arthur C. Clarke once joked that Asteroid 2001 should be named for him, after his novel *2001: A Space Odyssey*. Einstein beat him to it. Though Sir Arthur wasn't to go away empty-handed—in 1981, **Asteroid 4923** was given the designation "Clarke" in his honor.

Einsteinium

The chemical element that would later be given the name Einsteinium was first observed in 1952—appropriately enough in the blast debris left behind following the first ever **hydrogen bomb** test. Einsteinium is a highly radioactive (and highly toxic) element. It has 99 protons in its nucleus and, in its most stable form, 153 neutrons. This makes it an **extremely heavy** element—heavier even than the uranium used in nuclear fission plants. Given how nasty it is, it's probably no bad thing that Einsteinium **does not occur naturally** but has to be manufactured inside nuclear reactors (or through the actions of explosions) by bombarding samples of plutonium with neutrons. The element has no practical applications but is studied purely for research purposes.

The Einstein Cross

Perhaps the most fitting tribute to Einstein is a quasar in the constellation of Pegasus that goes by the name of the "**Einstein Cross**." Quasars are fiercely bright galaxies that lie at the very edge of the observable Universe—the Einstein cross is some **8 billion lightyears** from Earth, while the most distant quasar known is a staggering 12.7 billion lightyears away from us. The Einstein Cross is special because it's an example of a gravitational lens—something into which Einstein himself carried out the pioneering research. Four images of the quasar are actually visible—arranged in a cross shape—due to lensing by an intervening galaxy on the line of sight from Earth known as "**Huchra's lens**."

3-second Brief

Pre-eminent dead people tend to get things named after them. Einstein is no exception. An asteroid, a radioactive element, and an impossibly distant quasar all bear his moniker.

Related Thoughts

see also

EXTENDING THE GENERAL THEORY
page 90

ENERGY
page 114

"It is strange to be known so universally and yet to be so lonely."

Einstein Cross

Einsteinium, the product of a hydrogen bomb

New Einsteins

Richard Feynman

American physicist Richard Feynman was an active participant in the **Manhattan Project** to develop the US atomic bomb. His major contribution to physics came in the late 1940s when he helped to develop the work of Paul Dirac to create a quantum theory of the interaction between electromagnetic fields and charged particles—quantum electrodynamics, or QED. Like Einstein, Feynman was a flamboyant eccentric and an **original thinker**. Also like Einstein, Feynman was a late talker, not speaking until he was three years old. Perhaps that's why both men had a fondness for solving physics problems by thinking in pictures—Einstein with his thought experiments, Feynman with the **system of diagrams** that he pioneered for carrying out quantum theory calculations.

Stephen Hawking

Wheelchair-bound British physicist Stephen Hawking is probably the person most people think of when asked to name **Einstein's successor**: he's not only a genius, but one who's concentrated on Einstein's own areas of interest—gravitation and cosmology. In the 1970s Hawking discovered that black holes can radiate away quantum particles. His **dislike** of the notion of time travel mirrors Einstein's disdain for quantum theory. He has mused on the Big Bang, arguing that the Universe could be boundless not only in space but time as well, the so-called "**no boundary proposal**." And his research has also dealt with the ongoing problem of trying to unify gravity and cosmology.

Edward Witten

Not quite a household name, but regarded by many in his field as the greatest physicist at work today, American Edward Witten has made seminal contributions to string theory and the grander **M-theory**, in which the one-dimensional strings are replaced by higher-dimensional "membranes"—a theory he formulated in 1995. He is particularly concerned with unification models and the search for a theory of quantum gravity. Witten received the Fields Medal for mathematics in 1990, the **US National Medal of Science** in 2002, and the Isaac Newton Medal in 2010, among many other honors, and is widely tipped to bag a Nobel Prize before long. Which makes it all the more amazing that Witten didn't begin his professional life as a physicist, but worked instead as a journalist, only **retraining in physics** (his father's profession) during his early twenties.

3-second Brief

The twentieth century has produced a crop of great physicists since Einstein. But do any of them have the scientific brilliance to be called his rightful heir?

Related Thoughts

see also

MODERN UNIFICATION THEORIES
page 118

IS RELATIVITY WRONG?
page 126

NEW BLACK HOLES
page 134

"Most people say that it is the intellect which makes a great scientist. They are wrong: it is character."

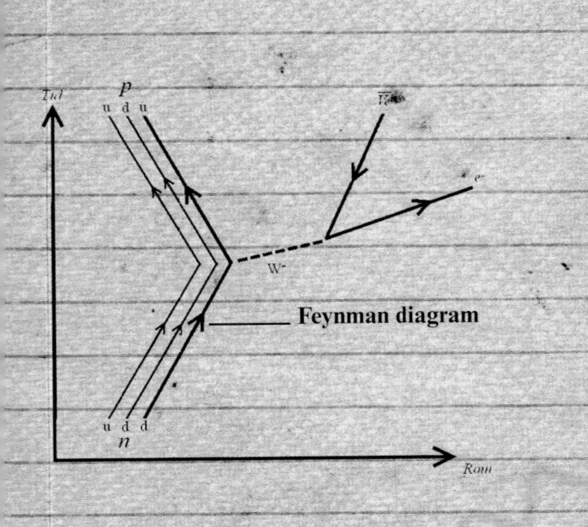

Richard Feynman

Stephen Hawking

Edward Witten

Popular Influence

Science celebrities

Einstein's overnight fame following the success of the general theory, and his sold-out lecture tours, gave rise to a **new phenomenon** in the public eye: the science celebrity. Ever since Einstein, many scientists—including Michio Kaku, Richard Feynman, and Richard Dawkins—have endeavored to explain their discoveries to the general public through lectures and popular-level books and articles. And, like Einstein, many have **achieved fame** to rival the more traditional celebrity fare of actors and musicians—just think Stephen Hawking or David Attenborough. Accordingly, factual science now makes for big-budget television—examples being Carl Sagan's landmark *Cosmos* series and the BBC's breathtaking *Planet Earth*. Meanwhile science books regularly top bestseller lists and win Pulitzer prizes, much of which has been attributed to the **rising prominence** of their authors.

Film and TV

Einstein himself has been the subject of many documentaries as well as dramatizations of his life—notably the BBC drama ***Einstein and Eddington***, which told the story of Einstein's formulation of the general theory of relativity and the eclipse measurements, made by British astronomer Arthur Eddington, which confirmed it. This portrayal has, however, been criticized by some science historians for taking too many liberties with the facts. Manifestly distorted views of Einstein's life have been presented in the comedy films ***IQ*** and ***Young Einstein***. While in *Star Trek: The Next Generation* android crew member Commander Data creates holographic likenesses of Einstein, Newton, and Stephen Hawking (played by himself) in order to stage the ultimate poker game. Einstein's face, in particular his eyes, also served as **inspiration** to the sculptors who created the puppets for *ET: The Extra-Terrestrial* and Yoda from the *Star Wars* movies.

Music

Einstein's influence has even extended to music—his persona and work forming the basis for many songs. These include **"Einstein A Go-Go"** (a hit for British band Landscape in 1981), "$E=mc^2$" (by Big Audio Dynamite, and which reached #11 in the UK singles chart in 1986), and "Quark, Strangeness and Charm" (the title track of a 1977 album by British rock band Hawkwind). Meanwhile, his life was the inspiration for Philip Glass's 1976 abstract opera ***Einstein on the Beach***. Einstein was also one of the influential figures depicted on the legendary cover of The Beatles' ***Sgt. Pepper's Lonely Hearts Club Band*** album—although he's largely obscured by John Lennon's right shoulder.

3-second Brief

Einstein's legacy leaves a lasting imprint on science, as well as politics, human rights, and—unlikely though it may seem—popular culture and the performing arts.

Related Thoughts

see also
THE RELUCTANT CELEBRITY
page 38
NEW EINSTEINS
page 142

"It should be possible to explain the laws of physics to a barmaid."

Popular Thought

Synonym for genius

The word "Einstein" has become synonymous with genius, and not just in popular culture—the Oxford English Thesaurus even lists it as such. Albert Einstein's rumpled appearance, crazy hair, and occasional wild expressions have made him into the blueprint for the **brilliant yet absent-minded** science professor. The view has been reinforced by other media with boffins in movies often conforming to Einstein's archetype of the **mad scientist** with a lovable side—from *Back to the Future*'s Emmett "Doc" Brown to Dr. Bunsen Honeydew in the Muppets. Einstein's disheveled appearance and bumbling manner underscored his humility and lack of pretence—and these are the qualities that **endeared** him to many. Hardly surprising it's a look that seems to have caught on.

Relativism

Einstein's revolutionary theories of relativity coincided with the rise of what became known as "relativism"—a **revolution in philosophy**, which rejected belief in absolute truths. The parallel was striking because, up until this time, Isaac Newton's rigid laws of motion and gravity, in which absolutes were paramount, had held sway—while at the same time the world seemed to be governed by social rules that were equally **inflexible**. Then in the early twentieth century came the First World War, the Russian revolutions, strikes—it was a period of great unrest that transformed the social order. This transformation was accompanied by a new age in science (not just relativity but quantum theory and the psychological ideas of Freud), as well as new thinking in art, literature, and music. Einstein, it seems, was truly a **child of his time**.

Myth busting

Like all celebrities, Einstein's private life was the subject of rumors—many of which turned out to be groundless myths. Perhaps the most common is that Einstein **failed math** at school. While it's true that he performed poorly in his undergraduate exams at Zurich Polytechnic, he actually excelled at math during his school days. Another falsehood is that much of the original work on the special theory was done by Einstein's first wife, **Mileva Maric**. She was, indeed, a competent physicist and mathematician—and checked many of Einstein's calculations—though historians agree the insight for relativity came solely from her husband. Then there's the story that Einstein once had an affair with **Marilyn Monroe**. Although Einstein is known to have had many extramarital affairs, Marilyn was not one of his conquests.

3-second Brief

Einstein, his life, and his theories are intertwined with the world's checkered social history, and have even made their impact felt on humble gossip.

Related Thoughts

see also
ZURICH POLYTECHNIC
page 28
A BEAUTIFUL MIND
page 44

"The hardest thing to understand in the world is the income tax."

Albert Einstein, 1939
Marilyn Monroe

Cultural Legacy

Albert Einstein Peace Prize

Einstein was an active campaigner for world peace, particularly in his later years after he saw the devastation that could be wrought by the atomic bomb. In 1979—the **100th anniversary** of his birth—the trustees of his estate elected to found the Albert Einstein Peace Prize Foundation. Its first action was to establish an annual prize of $50,000 to honor the individual who "has made the **greatest contribution** to world peace, consistent with **Einstein's philosophy**." Winners include former Canadian Prime Minister Pierre Trudeau, for his work on nuclear arms reduction, Willy Brandt, the former West German Chancellor who helped to negotiate peace with the east, and Joseph Rotblat, a campaigner for nuclear disarmament.

Hebrew University

It had long been the intention of Zionist Jews to establish a university in their homeland. The **Hebrew University of Jerusalem** was it. The campus opened officially in 1925 and Einstein was a member of its first board of governors. Upon his death, Einstein **bequeathed his papers** to the university along with all future royalties from his literary estate and from the use of his image in publications, as managed by the Corbis photo agency. Hebrew University also administers the Albert Einstein Archives, preserving Einstein's correspondence and other writings—amounting to over **40,000 documents**. The Archives have worked in close correspondence with the California-based Einstein Papers Project to collate and publish Einstein's writings in 25 volumes—10 of which have already been printed by Princeton University Press.

Albert Einstein Medal

The **Einstein medal** is an annual award recognizing physicists who have contributed to the fields in which Einstein himself worked. The first scientist to receive the prize, in 1979, was Stephen Hawking, of the University of Cambridge. Since then, recipients have included Edward Witten and John Archibald Wheeler, who was the mentor to Richard Feynman. The award is presented by the **Albert Einstein Society**, in Bern, Switzerland. Einstein resided in Bern between 1903 and 1905, and it was during this time that he formulated the special theory of relativity. The society maintains Einstein's old apartment in Bern—on the second floor of Kramgasse No. 49—and has restored it to look as it did when Einstein and his wife Mileva lived there. **Guided tours** of the residence are extremely popular—in 2009, it received over 30,000 visitors.

3-second Brief

Prizes awarded in his honor, his letters published, and the place where he first wrote down $E=mc^2$ now a museum—Einstein continues to enrich the world he left behind.

Related Thoughts

see also
THE ACTIVIST
page 54
NEW EINSTEINS
page 142

"Only a life lived for others is a life worthwhile."

Hebrew University of Jerusalem

Albert Einstein medal

New World Order

United Nations

Einstein's belief in a unified model of fundamental physics was mirrored in his vision for **world peace**—which he believed could only be achieved by unifying all the nations of the world under a single banner. Ideally, he thought that this should be done through the establishment of a **single world government**. Though even Einstein realized how impractical that was. Instead, he called for a "supranational organization" to be set up. It would have power over nation states and the military might to intervene and diffuse breaches of the peace before they led to serious conflict. The **United Nations**, established in 1945 at the end of the Second World War, went some way to realizing this vision—though Einstein felt it lacked the power and independence needed to be truly effective.

Globalization

Einstein's One World has been brought a step closer to reality by the globalization that's accompanied the rise of the **internet**. As people increasingly go online to interact with one another (through social networking sites like Facebook), to shop, read the news, play games, and even do business (via sites like eBay), so the borders that divide nation states are being **broken down**. In the "global village" of life online, it makes no difference whether you actually live in Arkansas or Azerbaijan. Accordingly, the laws governing people's activities online are, slowly but surely, having to adapt in order to **transcend these boundaries**. The effects of this are already being felt in the real world as culture, corporations, trends, and ideas all become global rather than national entities.

The rise of democracy

Albert Einstein lived through some of the darkest times of recent history—the First World War, the atrocities of Nazi Germany, and beginnings of the Cold War. Man's inhumanity to man, coupled with the looming specter of nuclear weapons, led Einstein to spend much of the final 10 years of his life striving not just for peace, but for **freedom of speech** and **individual liberty**. And, despite the current threats to peace from terrorism and the actions of rogue states, it seems much of the world has seen sense. In 1972, just 40 nations were free democracies—about 20 percent of the total number of countries in the world. By 2007 that figure had risen to 123, over **60 percent of the planet**. Einstein would be proud.

3-second Brief

Einstein spends his final years trying to unify not just physics, but the world too. The UN, the internet, and democratic freedom are now bringing his final dream to fruition.

Related Thoughts

see also
THE ACTIVIST
page 54
UNIFIED FIELD THEORY
page 100

"The only salvation for civilization and the human race lies in the creation of a world government."

Einstein visiting a High School in Philadelphia

United Nations Office, Geneva, Switzerland

Timeline

1932
Physicist Carl Anderson discovers the first ever particle of antimatter, which itself was predicted after applying relativity to subatomic particle theory.

1945
$E=mc^2$ is made horribly real when the first atom bomb to be used in anger explodes over the Japanese city of Hiroshima.

1947
Physicist William Shockley and colleagues invent the transistor, millions of which are now packed into every modern microchip. It works using semiconductors (for which Einstein helped to develop the theory in 1905).

1956
Peaceful use of the power of atoms is exemplified by the world's first nuclear power station, at Calder Hall in England.

1957
American physicist Charles Hard Townes applies Einstein's theory of stimulated emission by atoms to invent the laser, which is now used in everything from telecommunications to Blu-ray players.

1961
The first scalar-tensor theory, a modification to the general theory of relativity, is put forward by US physicists Carl Brans and Robert Dicke.

1969
String theory is formulated by Italian theoretical physicist Gabriele Veneziano. Some say strings are the most promising route by which to realize Einstein's dream of a unified field theory.

1974
Professor Stephen Hawking at the University of Cambridge shows that "black holes ain't so black," using quantum theory to show how they can emit radiation.

1982
A French team led by physicist Alain Aspect shows that quantum entanglement—a prediction of quantum theory that Einstein considered absurd—is a real feature of the world.

1986
Researchers led by Professor Kip Thorne at the California Institute of Technology show how wormholes—an idea developed by Einstein and colleagues—could, in principle, be used as time machines to the past.

1994
Miguel Alcubierre at the University of Wales, Cardiff develops a theoretical model, called the "warp drive," by which a spacecraft could greatly exceed the speed of light.

2008
The Large Hadron Collider (LHC) particle accelerator, on the Swiss-French border, is switched on for the first time. If anything can reveal whether the forces of nature really are unified, the LHC is it.

Glossary

Antimatter Subatomic particles that have opposite properties to those of normal matter. When matter and antimatter meet, they are converted into energy.

Asteroid Chunks of rock left over from the formation of the Solar System that continue to circle the Sun today.

Big Bang The event in which our Universe was created 13.7 billion years ago.

Bits "Binary digits" of information, which can be either "0" or "1."

Boson A subatomic particle with whole-number quantum spin, e.g. 0, 1, 2, 3, and so on.

Chemical element Any substance that has atoms as its fundamental constituent. Different elements are specified by the number of proton particles their atoms contain.

Cosmic ray A high-energy subatomic particle from outer space.

Electroweak theory A semi-unified particle physics theory that combines electromagnetism with the weak nuclear force—the force that operates within atomic nuclei and is responsible for radioactivity.

Fermion A kind of subatomic particle that has half-whole-number quantum spin, e.g. 1/2, 3/2, 5/2, and so on.

Gravitational redshift According to the general theory of relativity light loses energy climbing out of a gravitational field, lowering or "redshifting" its frequency.

Laser A source of light that's both monochromatic (one wavelength) and coherent (meaning the light waves are all in lockstep).

Lightyear The distance a light beam can travel in a year, equal to 5.9 million million miles (9.5 million million km).

Nuclear fission The release of energy by splitting the nucleus of a heavy atom.

Nuclear fusion The release of energy that occurs by joining together two light atomic nuclei.

Quantum entanglement The way in which pairs of quantum particles can remain linked even when separated by great distances.

Quantum gravity The general theory of relativity is a gravity theory that describes the universe. Meanwhile, the universe, according to the Big Bang theory, was once smaller than an atom. Therefore, there should exist a quantum theory of gravity to describe this phase of cosmic history. But so far, physicists are struggling to find it.

Qubits "Quantum binary digits," or qubits, of information can be "0" and "1" at the same time. They are used inside quantum computers.

Relativity paradox An apparent contradiction in the predictions of Einstein's theory of relativity. Paradoxes usually arise when the theory is not applied carefully enough.

Standard model Our current paradigm of particle physics and the fundamental forces of nature—suspected to be incomplete because it doesn't incorporate gravity.

Stimulated emission The process whereby atoms can be coaxed to give out light that is both coherent and monochromatic. The theory was first developed by Einstein and is fundamental to the operation of lasers.

String theory A proposed extension to the standard model of particle physics in which particles are composed of minute vibrating loops.

Supernova A colossal explosion marking the death of a massive star weighing many times the mass of the Sun.

Supersymmetry Subatomic particles split into two major families called fermions and bosons. Supersymmetry says that for every fermion there is a corresponding boson, and vice versa.

Topology A branch of mathematics that describes how points in space or on a surface are connected to other points.

Warp drive A theoretical method for traveling faster than light by stretching and deforming space.

Wormhole A tunnel through space that forms a shortcut between distant regions of the Universe.

3-Minute Summary

Early life

Albert Einstein was born on **March 14, 1879**, in Ulm, Germany. Although a late talker he became a bright child, with a keen interest in math and science—reading the great works of popular science aged 10. In 1896, Einstein enrolled at Zurich Polytechnic. He was a **brilliant yet lazy** student—only bothering with the topics that interested him—and finished second from bottom. This meant he was unable to get an academic job, so he took a post as a **technical expert** at the Swiss patent office. At Zurich, Einstein had met and fallen in love with Mileva Maric. They were **married in 1903** and had three children together.

Golden age

Einstein continued his scientific research in his spare time. The effort paid off in 1905, when he published four scientific papers, each of which **revolutionized physics**. One concerned the photoelectric effect—the basis of solar panels. Another set out his special theory of relativity—a new theory of motion for objects moving at close to light speed. And another dealt with a famous consequence of relativity: $E=mc^2$. The fourth dealt will Brownian motion. It was still three years before Einstein got his first academic job, a lectureship at the University of Bern. But this was followed in 1914 by an appointment to the prestigious University of Berlin. By 1915 Einstein had formulated the **general theory of relativity**, which explained gravity as curvature of space and time. It was confirmed experimentally in 1919. However, Einstein's workload had destroyed his personal life—he and Mileva separated in 1914, divorcing five years later.

Later years

Einstein married his second wife Elsa in 1919. Following the success of the general theory of relativity, he became **instantly famous**. Sold-out lectures were followed by the 1921 Nobel prize and a string of further accolades and distinctions. Yet Einstein spent much of his later life searching—in vain—for a theory to **unify** gravity with electricity and magnetism. His scientific judgment became conservative in middle-age, as he vehemently opposed the new and outlandish quantum theory. In the 1930s, Einstein's Jewish roots forced him to **flee Nazi Europe**. He settled in Princeton, New Jersey, where he continued his research and became active in the peace movement, which became a primary concern after the 1945 atomic bombings. Albert Einstein died from a ruptured aortic aneurysm on **April 18, 1955.**

"Our time is distinguished by wonderful achievements in the fields of scientific understanding and the technical application of those insights. Who would not be cheered by this? But let us not forget that human knowledge and skills alone cannot lead humanity to a happy and dignified life... What humanity owes to personalities like Buddha, Moses, and Jesus ranks for me higher than all the achievements of the enquiring and constructive mind."

Albert Einstein, 1910

Albert Einstein, 1947

Resources

Books

A Brief History of Time
Stephen Hawking
BANTAM BOOKS, 1995

The Collected Papers of Albert Einstein
Albert Einstein et al.
PRINCETON UNIVERSITY PRESS, 1987

Driving Mr Albert: A Trip Across America with Einstein's Brain
Michael Paterniti
DIAL PRESS, 2001

Einstein: His Life and Universe
Walter Isaacson
SIMON & SCHUSTER, 2007

Einstein's Daughter
Michele Zackheim
RIVERHEAD BOOKS, 1999

Einstein's Miraculous Year
Roger Penrose, Albert Einstein, and John Stachel
PRINCETON UNIVERSITY PRESS, 2005

The Elegant Universe
Brian Greene
VINTAGE, 2000

The God Particle: If the Universe is the answer, what is the question?
Leon Lederman
MARINER BOOKS, 2006

The Grand Design
Stephen Hawking
BANTAM, 2010

Quantum: A Guide for the Perplexed
Jim Al-Khalili
WEIDENFELD & NICOLSON, 2004

The Quantum Frontier: The Large Hadron Collider
Don Lincoln
JOHNS HOPKINS UNIVERSITY PRESS, 2009

Physics of the Impossible
Michio Kaku
ANCHOR BOOKS, 2009

The World As I See It
Albert Einstein
FILIQUARIAN PUBLISHING, 2007

Why Does $E=mc^2$?
Brian Cox and Jeff Forshaw
DA CAPO, 2010

Magazines/articles

"Beyond Einstein"
Scientific American, September 2004
www.scientificamerican.com

"Dark Energy: Was Einstein right all along?"
New Scientist, December 3, 2005
www.newscientist.com

"Einstein [In a nutshell]"
Discover, September 2004
www.discovermagazine.com

"Einstein's Blunders"
Focus, July 2010
www.bbcfocusmagazine.com

"Person of the Century"
Time, June 14, 1999
www.time.com

Web sites

The Albert Einstein Society
http://bit.ly/cXhtql

American Institute of Physics Einstein Exhibit
www.aip.org/history/einstein/

Einstein Archives Online
www.alberteinstein.info

Einstein Papers Project
www.einstein.caltech.edu

Einstein speaking on YouTube
http://bit.ly/dc4Hz3

Large Hadron Collider
www.lhc.ac.uk

LISA gravitational wave observatory
http://lisa.nasa.gov

What it looks like to fall into a black hole
http://bit.ly/anFlur

Index